IVAN PETROVICH PAVLOV
From a portrait by M. V. Nesterov

ACADEMY OF SCIENCES OF THE U.S.S.R

E. A. ASRATYAN

I. P. PAVLOV

HIS LIFE *and* WORK

University Press of the Pacific
Honolulu, Hawaii

I. P. Pavlov His Life and Work

by
E. A. Asratyan

ISBN: 0-89875-674-X

Reprinted from the 1953 edition

University Press of the Pacific
Honolulu, Hawaii
http://www.universitypressofthepacific.com

CONTENTS

1. FOREWORD

> ***"I. P. Pavlov was and remains one of those very rare organs, mightily and finely built, whose unceasing function is to unfold the mysteries of life. He is an amazingly integrate being, created by nature and work as if for the former to thus obtain knowledge of herself."***
>
> **A. M. GORKY**

In the severe November days of 1941 Joseph Vissarionovich Stalin cited Ivan Petrovich Pavlov among other illustrious men who brought fame to the Russian people.

Academician Pavlov was one of those scholars whose names live on through the ages. His long, intense and exceptionally fruitful scientific career not only made Russian physiology outstanding in the world, but created a new era in biology and medicine. This fact had to be acknowledged also by bourgeois scientists. The Dutch physiologist Jordan wrote that Pavlov's work made Leningrad a kind of Mecca, a place of pilgrimage for the physiologists of the world. The British scientist Berger, addressing Pavlov at the XV International Physiological Congress on behalf of the foreign delegations, said:

"I think there is no field in the natural sciences where one person is so outstanding as you are in the field of physiology."

At that Congress (1935) Pavlov was proclaimed the Princeps physiologorum mundi, i. e., the world's foremost physiologist. This was a triumph of Soviet science. It was another striking proof that in our socialist country the great Belinsky's prophetic words are being realized: "In the future, in addition to the victorious Russian sword, we shall lay the weight of Russian thought on the scales of European life. . . ."

Pavlov had to tread a thorny path in his life, one full of bitter trials, disappointments and relentless struggle. In the dark days of the tsarist regime when the universities were controlled despotically by bureaucrats of high and low rank, it was very difficult for such simple, direct, truthful and conscientious people of democratic views and unsubmissive nature as Pavlov to live and study and especially to carry on experimental work. His fate in this respect had much in common with that of other famous progressive Russian biologists, such as Sechenov, Mechnikov, Timiryazev and Michurin. But whereas Sechenov came to the end of his difficult unsettled life long before the Great October Socialist Revolution and Mechnikov died on its eve and moreover in a foreign land;* whereas Timiryazev had caught only a glimpse of the Soviet Era's first rays, Pavlov and also Michurin had the good fortune of living under Soviet rule for two decades. He was able to realize all his grand visions and cherished thoughts, to become an active participant in the building of our new joyous life and its ardent spokesman.

The history of physiology both native and foreign is certainly not lacking in noted scholars, but no name in that field shines so brilliantly as that of Ivan Petrovich Pavlov.

---

* Sechenov, Ivan Mikhailovich (1829-1905), resigned from the Medico-Chirurgical Academy in protest against the refusal to confirm I. Mechnikov professor in that Academy. He was subsequently professor in the universities of Odessa, Petersburg and Moscow.

Mechnikov, Ilya Ilyich (1846-1916), outstanding Russian biologist, owing to the difficulties set up by the tsarist government left Russia. Most of his life was spent in Pasteur's Institute in Paris.—*Ed.*

He is dear to every Soviet citizen. V. M. Molotov expressed the thoughts and sentiments of all Soviet people when he said at the banquet given in honour of the delegates of the XV International Physiological Congress in the Kremlin: "We are proud of the fact that Soviet physiologists are coming more and more to the fore among men of science; that among us such universally recognized authorities of natural science are working in this field as Academician Pavlov."

Not only scientists but all Soviet people commemorated as one of the notable dates in their glorious and heroic history the hundredth birthday anniversary of this giant of scientific thought and fiery patriot.

2. A SHORT BIOGRAPHY

> *"There is no broad highway in science and only those can reach its blazing peaks who fear not to become tired climbing its rocky paths."*
>
> K. MARX

Ivan Petrovich Pavlov was born on September 14 (old style), 1849, in the old Russian town, Ryazan. His father, Pyotr Dmitrievich Pavlov, was then a young priest of a poor parish and from all indications led a far trom well-to-do life. Descended from peasants, he had a passion for work in the orchard and vegetable garden. This, by the way, was a source of essential help to the restricted means of the family. He was a man of strong will and robust health, fond of intellectual work and a diligent reader of worldly books and magazines. The passion for physical and mental work, and other traits of his strong personality, he passed on to his sons, above all to his eldest—Ivan.

From early boyhood, Ivan helped his father in the garden and orchard, and his mother with her household duties, washing the dishes, bathing his younger brothers, etc. The love for physical work and sports remained with Pavlov throughout his life. To dig and fertilize the soil, to lay out and clean walks, plant and cultivate flowers, to ride a bicycle, row, swim and play *gorodki,* these were all Pavlov's beloved hobbies and he devoted his summer vacations to them. He was wont to say that physical work and sports gave him a singular feeling of "muscular gladness." At the venerable age of 86, he wrote to the miners of Donbas:

"Dear miners,

"All my life I have loved and still love work, mental and physical; and the latter perhaps even more than the former. But I felt a particular pleasure when I could combine with physical work the solution of a good hard problem, that is, unite my arms and head. You have taken that road. I wish you from my very heart to keep on treading further this road, the only one which provides happiness to man."

Ivan Petrovich had already learned to read and write on reaching the age of seven but owing to an accident which seriously affected his health (he fell from a high wall on a stone pavement, was seriously hurt and was ill for a long time) he went to school only four years later. This was the Ryazan church school. After completing it successfully he entered the local theological seminary. Several outstanding teachers, ardent supporters of the advanced ideas of that time, were members of the staff. They exerted a deep influence on the young Pavlov. Ivan Petrovich used to recall the seminary with a feeling of deep affection. He appreciated especially the absence of the callous, formal attitude towards students, so widespread in other such schools. He wrote in his short autobiography in 1904: "I recall it with gratitude. We had several excellent teachers.... In general, in the seminaries of that time (I don't know how it was afterwards) one had the possibility of following one's own intellectual inclinations, a possibility the absence of which had been felt so in the ill-famed Tolstoy Gymnasiums* (and, I think, also in the present ones)."

During Pavlov's student years progressive thought in

* After D Tolstoy, the tsarist Minister of Public Education, who converted the gymnasiums into scholastic schools with barrack-like discipline.—*Ed.*

Russia was in a state of turbulent development. The great democrats and enlighteners of the middle of the 19th century—Belinsky, Herzen, Chernyshevsky, Dobrolyubov, Pisarev—waged a severe, self-sacrificing battle against reactionary thought both in social life and in science; it was a fight to awaken the self-consciousness of the masses, a battle for freedom, for the realization of lofty progressive ideas. They also ardently propagated materialist concepts in the natural sciences, particularly biology. Great was the influence on youth of this brilliant group of revolutionary thinkers. And young Pavlov's noble, passionate and open heart was also captured by their ideas. He followed with eager interest the struggles of these progressive minds, zealously read their articles in the *Sovremennik, Russkoye Slovo* and other progressive journals and in particular their fiery articles on questions of natural science; he was taken up by their ideas on the importance of the natural sciences to social progress.

Pavlov wrote in the above-mentioned *Autobiography:* "Under the influence of the literature of the sixties, especially Pisarev, our intellectual interests turned to natural science and many of us including myself decided to go in for natural science in the university." In these years Pavlov was much influenced by the book, *Reflexes of the Brain*, the great work of the father of Russian physiology I. M. Sechenov, and by the Russian translation of Lewes' fascinating work, *Practical Physiology*.

Young Pavlov resolutely rejected an ecclesiastical career—which was the usual fate of theological seminary graduates. He left for St. Petersburg in 1870 without finishing the seminary on hearing that seminarists before completing their last year would be accepted in the universities. He matriculated in the physics and mathematics department, taking the natural sciences course. His excellence in studies and a certificate of poverty brought him a scholarship which, small as it was, still gave him his daily bread.

The course in physiology at the University of St. Petersburg was then given by Professor Ilya Fadeyevich Tsyon. This was not only a talented scientist and skilful experimenter but also a brilliant lecturer. Pavlov's interest in physiology, awakened while he was still a schoolboy, developed rapidly. Here is what he wrote in his *Autobiography*: "At that time the faculty was in a brilliant state. We had a number of professors of great authority in science with outstanding talents as lecturers. I chose for my major course animal physiology, and took chemistry as a minor. We physiologists were enormously impressed by Tsyon. We were truly fascinated by his ingeniously simple exposition of the most complex physiological questions and his masterful ability in conducting experiments. One can never forget such a teacher."

While still in his fourth year at the university, Pavlov, under Tsyon's direction and together with another student, Afanasiev, made his first research, which concerned the physiology of the nerves of pancreas. For this work he received a gold medal.

In 1875 Pavlov brilliantly completed the course at the university and obtained the degree of Candidate of Natural Sciences.

With ardent hopes the talented, energetic young scientist set out on the road of independent life, but only to meet with bitter disillusionment. Conditions of work for young scientists were extremely hard in those dark days of tsarist Russia. It was difficult to find a position. As a rule the universities were controlled by servile hirelings of the prevailing regime; outstanding intellectuals were persecuted; there were endless intrigues and unscrupulous strife among various groupings of professors. Naturally, the ones who suffered most from this state of affairs were the courageous, honest, progressive scientists, those who were thinking not of how to adapt themselves to fortuitous external circumstances, but how best to serve their native science. Among such victims were the great scientists Sechenov and Mechnikov. Such also was Pavlov. He was able to overcome all obstacles only because of his physical strength and moral firmness, his endurance, unfaltering will, amazing capacity for work, flaming patriotism and intense love of science.

It may have seemed at first that fortune smiled favourably on the young graduate. His teacher Tsyon, who had just received the chair in physiology at the Medico-Chirurgical Academy (as the Military Medical Academy was then called), which had been left by Sechenov, invited Pavlov to become his assistant. At the same time Pavlov enrolled in the third-year course of the Academy—as he wrote in his *Autobiography*, "not to become a physician, but in order, having obtained the degree of doctor of medicine, to have the right afterwards to a chair in physiology... although the professorship itself appeared as something beyond grasp, incredible." But soon Pavlov, because of the appointment of Tarkhanov in Prof. Tsyon's place, considered it necessary to leave the department and thus lost not only an excellent place for scientific work but also his income.

Fortunately, after some time he obtained a position as laboratory assistant to Professor Ustimovich at the physiological department of the Veterinary Institute. Simultaneously he continued his studies at the Medical Academy. In Ustimovich's laboratory (1876-1878) Pavlov made a series of valuable investigations on blood circulation. Here the first signs of his noted scientific method, viz., to study the functions of the intact organism under natural conditions, made their appearance. After many trials he succeeded in measuring the blood pressure of dogs without narcosis and without tying them to the operation table. While working in that laboratory Pavlov was able to lay aside a small sum of money and to go to Breslau in the summer of 1877 in order to acquaint himself with the work of the well-known physiologist, Professor Heidenhain.

In 1878 Professor Botkin, the famous Russian clinician, invited the gifted young physiologist to work in the physiological laboratory at his clinics formally as a laboratory worker, but actually as its chief.

In 1879 Ivan Petrovich graduated from the Academy, with the award of a gold medal for his research work. There he won a two-year fellowship for postgraduate work. Thus he could now devote all his time to research work at Botkin's clinics.

Pavlov worked in a small house, built either as a janitor's lodging or a bathhouse, and completely unfit for research work. Here, with no laboratory equipment even of the simplest kind, always in need of money to buy animals for experiments, Pavlov developed an enthusiastic activity. In this, his first laboratory, he spent more than ten years—until 1890. (In 1886 he became its official chief.) The almost complete independence of his research allowed Pavlov to unfold his original talent and give full swing to his creative genius. His enormous capacity for work was fully demonstrated here as well as his indomitable will and unfailing energy, bringing him outstanding results both theoretical and practical. Engaged in studying the physiology of blood circulation and digestion, and also certain pharmacological problems, he quickly matured as a theoretician and experimenter as well as organizer and director of large and complex scientific projects.

Pavlov's life during the years spent at the laboratory was full of privation and family troubles but nonetheless he considered that period to be unusually significant and fruitful. He always recalled it with a particularly warm feeling. "In spite of certain unfavourable circumstances in this laboratory," he wrote in his *Autobiography*, "the chief of which were, of course, its scanty means, I consider that the time spent there was very beneficial for my future in science. First of all—complete independence and then the opportunity of devoting myself entirely to laboratory work."

Ivan Petrovich always remembered Botkin with a feeling of gratitude; this was not only because the latter gave him the opportunity to work and grow as a scientist, but also because he rendered him strong ideological support. The development of Pavlov's scientific principles was greatly influenced by Botkin's theories on the important role of the nervous system both in the normal and pathological activity of the organism, and his views on the need for the closest union between experimental physiology and clinical medicine. Pavlov wrote: "S. P. Botkin embodied in the highest degree the legitimate and fruitful union between medicine and physiology, these two forms of human activity which are building, before our eyes, the edifice of the science of the human organism and promise in the future to furnish man with his greatest happiness—health and life."

Among Pavlov's achievements of that period was his research on the efferent cardiac nerves. It became the theme of his doctor's dissertation which he submitted in 1883. It brought him a gold medal, the title of docent and a two years' sojourn at Heidenhain's laboratory in Breslau, and Ludwig's in Leipzig (1884-1886). In this period he developed an ingenious and original method of isolating the heart and lungs, leading to the solution of many important theoretical and practical problems both in the physiology of blood circulation and in pharmacology. In this exceptionally fruitful period, following his return to the homeland, Ivan Petrovich laid a solid foundation for his future studies on digestion, namely, he discovered the nerves controlling the secretion of the pancreas and carried out his classical experiment on sham feeding.

These and other scientific achievements made Pavlov's name famous both in Russia and abroad. But the joy of his scientific success and the satisfaction at its high appraisal were marred by his material straits and the very limited possibilities of his modest laboratory. And then came the dark prospect of losing even this hovel.

The financial and other material difficulties aggravated by Pavlov's complete helplessness in matters of everyday life began to be felt especially after his marriage in 1881. Little is known about this difficult phase of Ivan Petrovich's life and he did not like to tell about it. However, we do read in his *Autobiography* that he, "already married and possessed of a son, was always in a bad way with respect to money." We know of these troubles, poisoning the life of the great scientist, mainly from the tales of his friends and students of that time and from the recently published memoirs of his wife, Serafima Vasilievna.

Here are a few characteristic episodes.

In Serafima Vasilievna's memoirs concerning the first year of their married life, we read: "When we returned to Petersburg from the country we had absolutely no money. And were it not for Dmitri Petrovich's (Ivan Petrovich's brother who was an assistant to D. I. Mendeleyev.—*E. A.*) apartment, we would actually have had no place where to lay our heads."

The same year he obtained his doctor's degree, Ivan Petrovich's first son was born, whom the happy parents named Mirchik. In the summertime both wife and child had to be taken to the country. But Ivan Petrovich had no means for renting a country house near Petersburg, so they had to leave for the far south to his wife's sister who lived in a remote village.

Pavlov did not even have enough money for their railway ticket. "Ivan Petrovich and Dmitri Petrovich could hardly scrape together enough money for a ticket to Ryazan and wrote a letter to their father requesting him to furnish me with the money for the journey further." Ivan Petrovich's son fell sick and died in that forsaken village, leaving his parents in deep mourning. The loss was especially painful because Serafima Vasilievna's first pregnancy had ended in a miscarriage, probably not without the influence of the poor living conditions.

From other sources we know that owing to the financial difficulty he experienced, Ivan Petrovich lived for a time not with his family, but in the laboratory. Professor Chistovich, then working under Pavlov in Botkin's clinics, recalled another incident:

"At one time Ivan Petrovich suffered from a complete lack of money and was forced to live alone, separated from his family, in the apartment of a friend, N. P. Simanovski. We, collaborators and followers of Pavlov, knew of his hard material condition and conceived of a plan to help him. We invited him to give us a series of lectures on the innervation of the heart, collected among ourselves a sum of money and gave it to him as if to meet the expenses of the course. But nothing came of it. He spent all the money in buying animals for the course and left nothing for himself."

This devotee of science would often spend his own scanty salary to buy animals and to satisfy other requirements of experimental work when he himself was in dire need. Such were the demands of his beloved science; for in those days "the constant necessity to pay for every experimental animal," he bitterly wrote in his autobiography, "at a time when there was in general a scarcity of financial means, told heavily on the laboratory work."

In addition to all this, there was absolutely no guarantee of the future. Had he not already found himself once in the street because no position was open in Botkin's department? And he was at that time a doctor of medicine and a recognized investigator! What would have happened to him then if Professor V. A. Manassein had not given him a place in his department? Where was the assurance that such a story with even sadder outcome would not be repeated?

Pavlov was not very practical in personal matters. For a long time he vainly searched for a new position. He applied for the chair of physiology at the University of St. Petersburg (vacant after Sechenov had left), but his application was rejected. Following this stroke of ill fortune, the source of much grief to Pavlov, he again felt the bitter taste of humiliation. The reactionary tsarist minister Delyanov refused to sanction his appointment to the chair of physiology at the Tomsk University. Instead, Delyanov gave this position to a little-known scientist, Veliki. Some other minister had solicited for the latter. This outrageous incident gave rise to protests by progressive medical circles. Thus, an article appeared in the newspaper *Vrach* which stated: "A doctor of zoology, Veliki, has been appointed to the chair of physiology at Tomsk.... We cannot but express our deep regret that the earlier intention to appoint to this chair the private lecturer in physiology at the Academy, Pavlov, had not been realized. Pavlov for a long time has been justly considered as one of the best physiologists in Russia, and there are a great many reasons for his preeminence. He is not only a doctor of medicine but also a candidate of natural science and moreover he has uninterruptedly been working and helping others in their work in Botkin's clinics. We know, by the way, that the failure to appoint Pavlov has amazed such an experienced judge in these matters as Prof. S. M. Sechenov."

Eventually, the physiologist Pavlov was elected to the chair of pharmacology at the Tomsk University and then at the University of Warsaw. But Ivan Petrovich went to neither place. Soon after (in 1890) he was appointed

Professor of Pharmacology at the Military Medical Academy and occupied this position for five years, until his transfer to the chair of physiology in the same academy in 1895. Ivan Petrovich headed this latter department continuously for three decades.

An important event in Pavlov's personal life and scientific career was the invitation to organize and direct the department of physiology in the new Institute of Experimental Medicine (1891). He remained at the head of that department for 45 years—till the end of his life. It was mainly here that he carried out his classical experiments on the digestive glands which soon made him famous throughout the world. Here too he conducted a major part of his work on conditioned reflexes, work which immortalized his name and brought glory to the science of his country.

At last in 1901, Ivan Petrovich was elected corresponding member of the Academy of Sciences and in 1907—a member. The modest physiological laboratory in the Imperial Academy of Sciences did not play any essential role in Pavlov's scientific achievements before the October Revolution. But then the superb institute, organized by the Soviet Government (in 1924) in its place, soon became a centre for the development of his immortal materialist theory of the higher nervous activity.

Before the October Revolution, Pavlov heroically made his way in science through strenuous effort, suffering many privations and sacrifices. The continuous struggle with difficulties in his scientific work and adversity in his personal life, developed his creative genius, hardened his will to win, made him the more eager to serve his countrymen and strengthened his belief in a better future for his beloved fatherland. One cannot help noting in this connection a highly characteristic trait of Pavlov's prerevolutionary life—almost all his scientific achievements received formal recognition by official institutions of tsarist Russia only long after they had been recognized by the progressive minds of our country and abroad. At the very same time when the dull and reactionary tsarist minister refused to confirm Pavlov's appointment to the chair of physiology, Sechenov, Ludwig, Heidenhain and other scientists considered him as an outstanding physiologist. Pavlov became a professor of physiology only on reaching his 46th year. He became a member of the Academy of Sciences only three years after he received the Nobel Prize.

Pavlov's financial difficulties and domestic troubles noticeably declined after his appointment to the Institute of Experimental Medicine and entirely vanished when he was elected to the professorship at the Military Medical Academy and became a member of the Academy of Sciences. But conditions for his scientific work and the attitude of tsarist officials toward it remained unfavourable as before. Pavlov especially felt the need of permanent collaborators. There were no more than five or six of them in all the organizations under his guidance. Only two or three were in the physiological department of the Institute of Experimental Medicine. He himself paid out of his own pocket the salary of practically the only assistant in the laboratory of the Imperial Academy of Sciences. In the Military Medical Academy the number of his collaborators was very limited, owing to the hostile attitude, among other things, toward Pavlov of the War Minister and the chiefs of the Academy. He incurred their hatred because of his democratic views, his unceasing struggle against the despotism of the tsar's officials, his constant support of the students' interests; because, with the whole of his honest, sensitive soul, he was closely bound to the common people and also because he was developing a materialist theory of higher nervous activity.

Only through very great efforts did he succeed in retaining his most gifted pupils in the department and in securing scholarships for them for trips abroad. Even Pavlov himself, already at that time one of the greatest authorities among Russian physiologists, for long was not formally confirmed to the title of professor-in-ordinary. He was the only chief of a theoretical faculty not to receive a government apartment. The intrigues against Pavlov, known to the whole world as "Russia's great physiologist," according to Timiryazev, did not cease until the October Revolution, although his world-wide authority in physiology caused the officials to treat him with hypocritical courtesy. At the same time they conspired to discredit a number of dissertations submitted by Pavlov's collaborators and seldom confirmed the degrees and appointments of his followers. They were constantly inciting all manner of society ladies against him, who cried about the "sinfulness" of his experiments on animals; they caused his defeat in the elections to the presidency of the Society of Russian Physicians in spite of his great activity in that organization, etc.

Pavlov's constant need of assistants was met to a certain extent by enthusiasts who volunteered their aid without remuneration. His authority, outstanding scientific achievements, ardent patriotism and democratic views attracted like a magnet many zealous helpers—students of the Military Medical Academy as well as physicians assigned to the Institute of Experimental Medicine and also physicians from various parts of the country and from abroad. True, these collaborators were only temporary and the changes in the staff made it difficult for Pavlov to plan and carry out large-scale scientific projects. But they did much to help him realize his ideas.

There were many great difficulties too in financing the organizations under his guidance. Ivan Petrovich had to appeal to the general public and to cultural societies for private contributions to his laboratories. And help did come. It was with such aid, for instance, that he was

I. P. Pavlov and his brother D. P. Pavlov in student years

The Home of Pavlov. Above can be seen the room in which Pavlov spent the first years of his life as seminarist. In the foreground is Pavlov surrounded by his relatives and fellow countrymen of Ryazan

I. P. Pavlov playing *gorodki*

able to begin construction of the famous "tower of silence"—the special laboratory for studying the conditioned reflexes of dogs. However, the building was not finished until after the October Revolution.

There is nothing strange about this. All science was in such an unenviable position in tsarist Russia. Pavlov met with the same bitter fate as Lomonosov, Mendeleyev, Pirogov, Sechenov, Mechnikov, Timiryazev, Michurin—these great sons of their country, who brought it glory through their self-sacrificing fight for the triumph of their native science.

But Pavlov was luckier than most of these celebrated representatives of Russian science and culture. He had the fortune to witness the downfall of the hated tsarist regime and after the Great October Revolution to realize his great research plans.

During the early days of the Revolution, when the country was still in the throes of hunger and privation and when our heroic people led by the Communist Party were waging a severe fight for the young Soviet State, Vladimir Ilyich Lenin issued a special government decree which revealed the exceedingly warm sympathy and care for Pavlov and his work by the Communist Party and the Soviet Government.

This decree noted the "outstanding scientific contributions of Academician I. P. Pavlov, which are of enormous significance to the working people of the whole world." A commission headed by M. Gorky was organized "to create in the shortest time the most favourable conditions for the scientific work of Academician Pavlov and his collaborators." The corresponding government organizations were: "to publish in a de-luxe edition the scientific work prepared by Academician Pavlov ... to furnish Academician Pavlov and his wife with a special ration" and supply his laboratory and apartment with the maximum accommodations. This historic decree of Lenin was an expression of faith in the venerable Russian scientist and patriot of the young Soviet State.

Afterwards, the quick growth of the country's economic power gave the Soviet Government the means to create in a short time the most favourable conditions for the development of the great scholar's scientific work.

The "tower of silence" in the Institute of Experimental Medicine was finished. His 75th birthday was honoured by the establishment of a new physiological institute, now bearing his name, in the Academy of Sciences of the U.S.S.R.; his 80th, by the construction of a special "City of Science" in the village of Koltushi at the outskirts of Leningrad. This institution, the only one of its kind in the world, also bears his name. Clinics for treating nervous and psychical diseases were attached to his institutes, thus realizing his old dream of uniting theory and practice. All of his institutes were equipped with the most up-to-date apparatus. His permanent staff both scientific and technical increased manifold. He received considerable sums above the ordinary budgetary allotments to be spent at his own discretion. The scientific works of his laboratories were published regularly.

Pavlov was loved by the people. He had the powerful material and moral support of the Soviet Government. The 85th birthday of the great scientist was marked, among other measures, by the granting of new large sums for the further advancement of his researches.

Greeting Ivan Petrovich, the Sovnarkom (Council of People's Commissars) of the U.S.S.R. wrote:

"To Academician I. P. Pavlov:

"On your 85th birthday the Council of People's Commissars of the U.S.S.R. sends you its warm greetings and congratulations. The Sovnarkom especially notes your inexhaustible energy in scientific work, the successes of which have deservedly placed your name among the classics of natural science.

"The Sovnarkom wishes you health, vigour and long years of fruitful work for the benefit of our great country."

The sharp contrast between the attitude towards his work on the part of tsarism and of the socialist state could not but stir the great thinker. Pavlov, who under the tsarist regime always lacked adequate means for experimentation, was now constantly concerned whether he could prove worthy of the faith placed in him by the Soviet Government and whether he could justify the enormous sums granted for his work. All this he declared publicly and to every one. A striking example of this were his words at the reception in the Kremlin by the Soviet Government for the delegates of the XV International Physiological Congress which had taken place in 1935 both in Leningrad and Moscow. "We, in charge of scientific institutes," he said, "are actually in a state of anxiety and uneasiness whether we shall be able to justify all those sums which are placed at our disposal by the Government." On another occasion he declared with great feeling: "How I would like to live for long, because my laboratories are flourishing as never before. The Soviet state has given millions for my scientific work and for the construction of laboratories. I want to believe that the measures for aiding the workers in physiology, and I, after all, am a physiologist, will reach their goal and my science will bloom on my native soil."

His anxieties were in vain. Unfolding the eagle's wings of his great genius Pavlov built in the main the wonderful edifice of the materialist theory of the higher nervous activity.

The great naturalist was in his 87th year when the thread of his life was broken. He died unexpectedly of pneumonia. In spite of his venerable age, he had been of robust strength, full of intense energy, had worked unceasingly, had been enthusiastically making plans for further studies and least of all had been thinking of death....

3. PAVLOV AS MAN AND CITIZEN

Ivan Petrovich was unusually endowed with nobility of character. In him were reflected some of the best traits of the great Russian people, whom he loved so dearly. Modest and exceptionally simple in manner, he was highly responsive, accessible, and sociable both in his personal life and work. There was a friendly atmosphere in the scientific institutes under his guidance and he was the heart and soul of any gathering—whether a gymnastics group, the Society of Russian Physicians or a group of his collaborators. He had the gift of attracting people and uniting them into a friendly circle. There was nothing that he would begrudge his collaborators. If in the first years after the revolution, during the famine, he chanced to receive a food parcel, he would take it to the laboratory and share it with everyone.

Pavlov's great understanding and sympathy, his transparent honesty and directness in large and small matters made him exceptionally charming. He was loved by his friends and pupils and was respected by his opponents in science.

Pavlov was exceedingly punctual and accurate in his work and everyday life. One could set a watch by his arrival at the laboratory. He was very strict with himself and would not stand any laxity in others, especially in scientific matters. If an experiment suffered because of the carelessness of an assistant, Pavlov would become highly indignant and could find very caustic remarks for the culprit.

Pavlov's animated and even impetuous character was an unfailing source of energy. These traits served to inspire all with whom he came in contact. His enthusiastic temperament made itself felt not only in scientific work, during operations and experiments, and in discussions, but also in sports, in his gardening, as a collector and in his everyday life. He was like a youth in his enthusiasm at work, in his alertness and endurance; to the very end he retained his phenomenal memory, his sharp, penetrating mind, and a broad interest in scientific and social life. His special attachment for the youth among his collaborators was also a reflection of his own youthful spirit.

Pavlov used to speak in a very clear, simple, concise, and picturesque manner. He had a pleasant, sonorous voice and while talking, he gesticulated vehemently. He was a wonderful conversationalist and a warm and witty debater. His laugh was loud, straightforward, and contagious.

Pavlov also knew how to rest and relax. During the summer months he parted almost entirely from science. According to his wife, "... not a single scientific book had an entry leave to the country house. Ivan Petrovich considered it necessary to free his mind entirely of all laboratory thoughts." During his summer vacation he read only fiction and devoted himself to the garden and orchard, to swimming and athletic games. Physical work was a source of real pleasure to him. "I don't know who I would rather be," he said, "a farmer, a furnaceman or a scientist." He was a man of high culture, exceptionally well-read and of extensive interests in life. He had a keen fancy for making collections, the choice of objects changing with time. He collected butterflies, plants, stamps and towards the end of his life—paintings. According to L. A. Orbeli, Pavlov at one time systematically visited all art exhibitions. He was also interested in music and liked friendly card games.

Ivan Petrovich did not smoke or drink and led a very simple life.

Although he was, as he himself liked to say, a man of science, "from head to foot," he did not isolate himself from social life. He was for many years a very active vice-president of the Society of Russian Physicians and subsequently its president. He was the organizer and head for many years of the Physicians' Gymnastic Society, and a member (afterwards the president) of the Honour Court of the Petersburg Physicians' Society of Mutual Aid. During the last years of his life he directed the formation of the Physiological Society, the foundation of the *Journal of Physiology* and the organization of a number of congresses. At the XIV International Physiological Congress in Rome (1932) he proposed in the name of the Soviet Government to hold the next congress in our country and the proposal was unanimously accepted by the delegates. And it was he who directed the preparation for the XV International Congress in Leningrad and Moscow (1935) and headed its work.

Ivan Petrovich was an ardent patriot in the highest sense of the word. He loved his fatherland, and the fine culture and traditions of the Russian people with a deep and self-sacrificing passion. He loved the works of the great Russian writers, musicians, artists and scientists, the military glory of the country, and its customs. He also treated with respect the dignity, traditions and culture of other peoples. He immediately grasped and greatly esteemed the policy of the Soviet Government towards the various nationalities.

In 1927, when he had to undergo an operation for gallstones, and a council of our noted professors suggested that a certain distinguished German surgeon be invited for this purpose, he emphatically protested, declaring: "I do not consider at all that the German surgeons are better than ours and I will in no case allow a German to operate on me, when the flower of our surgery is present here." He was brilliantly operated on by Professor Martynov.

When abroad, Ivan Petrovich would feel exceedingly lonesome for his native land and make haste to come home. His return was always a happy occasion for him. Serafima Vasilievna recollected how once, returning from one of his trips abroad, Ivan Petrovich at the border station lifted his hat and bowed down deeply to his native soil.

Raised in the spirit of the great Russian revolutionary democrats of the 19th century, Pavlov was a man of progressive democratic principles. He was connected to the working people with the whole of his noble soul. He considered work to be a virtue and hated idlers. When he was awarded the Nobel Prize, a certain businessman tried to persuade him to invest some of the money he had received in stock exchange speculation, promising large profits. Ivan Petrovich answered indignantly: "I have earned this money by unceasing scientific work, and science never had, does not have, nor ever will have anything to do with the Stock Exchange."

Pavlov did not participate in the direct political fight against the autocracy, but his strongly negative attitude towards tsarism constantly came to the fore in his struggles against the reactionaries in the scientific and higher educational institutions of tsarist Russia. According to the reminiscences of his wife and of the older generation of his pupils (V. V. Savich, L. A. Orbeli, I. S. Tsitovich and others), while still in the first years of his professorship, Pavlov sympathized with the students' revolutionary movement and supported the so-called "students' disorders." He persistently fought for many years against the despotism of the head of the Military Medical Academy and the tyranny of the tsarist officials. After the shameful defeat of tsarism in the Russo-Japanese war, when reaction was raging unrestrainedly, Pavlov's patriotic feelings were sorely offended and he regarded with sympathy the rising tide of revolution. "No," he said, "only a revolution can save Russia. The government which brought the country to such a disgrace must be overthrown."

It was not without cause that during the ceremony when Pavlov received the Nobel award in 1904, the king of Sweden declared: "I am afraid of your Pavlov. He wears no decorations. He is evidently a socialist."

In 1913, after the "students' disorders," the Minister of War ordered the expulsion of 1,500 students from the Military Medical Academy. Ivan Petrovich with four other professors made an energetic protest and according to some evidence he threatened to resign. A very interesting illustration of his political feelings was his letter to the first Russian Physiological Congress. Its chief organizer, he had vainly sought help from official institutions under the old regime in convoking it, and it was held only in April 1917. Ivan Petrovich wrote: "We have just parted with the dark, oppressing times. It is enough to tell you that this congress of ours did not receive sanction to be held on Christmas and was allowed to be called on Easter only because the members of its organizational committee had signed a statement that no political resolutions would be presented at the congress. And that was insufficient. Two or three days before our revolution, final permission was obtained with the proviso that the theses of the scientific reports be handed to the city head the day before the opening. Thank God that this belongs to the past and let us hope the irrevocable past."

Patriot and true democrat, Ivan Petrovich, from the first years after the Great October Socialist Revolution,

I. P. Pavlov during a discussion

I. P. Pavlov cleaning a path in his garden

welcomes with all his heart the fact that in our country "the absurd and monstrous abyss," as he said, "between the rich and poor has been done away with," and that here "social wealth is distributed among individuals according to their work." He was proud that the Russian people had the fairest policy in world history toward nationalities, having established true equality and national brotherhood in our land of many peoples. There is no need to mention how great was his enthusiasm over the care of the Communist Party and the Soviet Government for the growth of science and culture in our country.

Pavlov followed very intently the creative efforts of peaceful construction taking place according to Lenin's and Stalin's plans. He had become convinced that socialism was, as he expressed it, an imposing "Mr. Fact."

Who does not know his passionate, highly patriotic speech at the opening of the XV International Physiological Congress in 1935 in Leningrad? Speaking of the growing war danger and of the fact that "war is essentially a bestial method of settling difficulties, a method unworthy of the human mind with its unlimited resources," Pavlov, joyfully and proudly, added: "And I am happy that the Government of my great fatherland, in its fight for peace, for the first time in history proclaimed: 'not one inch of foreign soil.' "

In 1935, after a long absence, he paid a visit to his native city, Ryazan. His fellow citizens gave a banquet in his honour. He replied to their cordial reception and greetings in words of deep feeling: "I want to say that representatives of science had been honoured before, also. But this expression of esteem had taken place within the limits of a narrow circle of men of the same type, so to say, men of science. That which I behold now is very different from these restricted ceremonials. At present science is honoured among us by all the people. I saw this in the morning when met at the station and in the kolkhoz and when I travelled here. This is not a casual incident. I think I shall not be mistaken if I say that this is an achievement of the Government of my country. Before, science had been cut off from life, alienated from the people. Now I behold quite a different thing—the whole people is honouring and prizing science. I raise my cup and drink to the only government in the world which so prizes science, and supports it so warmly—to the Government of my country."

Not long before his death he spoke these moving words: "Whatever I do, I always think that I am, thereby, as much as my strength allows me, serving first of all my country. An immense social change is now taking place in my country.... I want to live until the time when I shall see the final results of this social change. A colossal achievement of the Soviet Government is its unceasing strengthening of the country's defensive capacity. I want to live for many and many years too, because I am certain of the security of my native land."

Pavlov hated the fascist warmongers. His speech at the XV International Physiological Congress was a flaming expression of this hatred. It was a passionate appeal for relentless struggle against the barbarity of fascism. In the last years of his life, when the aggressive tendencies of the fascist vandals and obscurantists came more and more to light, he spoke very often and with a solemn anger and hatred for them. He was soundly convinced that our heroic people at the head of the other freedom-loving peoples of the world would save civilization from the fascist plague. Some months before his death, the great patriot declared: "Now, I often regret more and more that, engaged in scientific work, I did not roam about in the Soviet country. But I am questioning everybody. These days, my collaborators who have been to the Central Asian republics and in the Far East have returned. I am fascinated by their accounts. The once backward peoples are now literate, educated, and are becoming more and more well-to-do. In a war we shall be defending our true fatherland, our culture, our science. The whole people will rise to defend their country."

With what exuberant joy he would have met the brilliant victory of the Soviet people over fascist Germany and imperialist Japan; how proud he would have been of the wisdom of our Government in its victorious fight against the new warmongers, had he lived to our days!

4. PAVLOV AS SCIENTIST AND TEACHER

Pavlov attained the summits of science not only because of his brilliant talent, the unconquerable force of his powerful mind, but also because of his rare traits as a scientist, his high integrity in research. These qualities made him an unsurpassed organizer and guide of scientific research, and an outstanding educator of a new generation of physiologists.

Above all must be noted Pavlov's unlimited devotion to science. Dedicating himself to materialist science while still a youth, under the impression of the progressive ideas in natural science propagated by the great Russian enlighteners and democrats of the middle of the last century, he remained true to it all his long life. Science was his element. He lived in science and loved it passionately. Scientific creation was the source of his greatest joy. He wrote about this in his *Autobiography*: "I have received all that can be demanded of life: the complete realization of those principles with which I have entered it. I dreamed of finding life's happiness in intellectual work, in science—and I did find it and am finding it there." The interests of science of his native land were like a compass to him in his personal and public activity. He expressed his attitude to science in the wonderful "Letter to the Youth" of our country. "Remember," he wrote, "that science requires of an individual the price of his whole life.

ПОСТАНОВЛЕНИЕ

СОВЕТА НАРОДНЫХ КОМИССАРОВ

Принимая во внимание совершенно исключительные научные заслуги академика И.П. ПАВЛОВА, имеющие огромное значение для трудящихся всего мира, СОВЕТ НАРОДНЫХ КОМИССАРОВ П О С Т А Н О В И Л

1. Образовать на основании представления Петросовета специальную Комиссию с широкими полномочиями в следующем составе тов. М. Горького, Заведывающего Высшими учебными Заведениями Петрограда тов. Кристи и члена Коллегии Отдела Управления Петросовета тов. Каплуна, которой поручить в кратчайший срок создать наиболее благоприятные условия для обеспечения научной работы академика Павлова и его сотрудников.

2.- Поручить Государственному Издательству в лучшей типографии Республики отпечатать роскошным изданием заготовленный академиком Павловым научный труд, сводящий результаты его научных работ за последние 20 лет, причем оставить за академиком И.П. Павловым право собственности на это сочинение как в России, так и за-границей.

3.-Поручить Комиссии по Рабочему снабжению предоставить академику Павлову и его жене специальный паек, равный по калорийности двум академическим пайкам.

4. Поручить Петросовету обеспечить профессора Павлова и его жену пожизненным пользованием занимаемой ими квартирой и обставить ее и лабораторию академика Павлова максимальными удобствами.

Председатель Совета
Народных Комиссаров.

Москва, Кремль
24-го Января 1921 года

The Decree of the Sovnarkom of Jan. 24, 1921

DECREE
OF THE COUNCIL OF PEOPLE'S COMMISSARS

In view of the exceptionally outstanding scientific contributions of Academician I. P. PAVLOV, which are of enormous significance to the working people of the whole world, the COUNCIL OF PEOPLE'S COMMISSARS has DECREED that

1) a special commission be organized with wide powers, and in conformity with the proposal of the Petrograd Soviet to consist of the following members: Comrade M. Gorky, the Chief of the Higher Schools in Petrograd Comrade Christi, and the member of the Board of Administration of the Petrograd Soviet Comrade Kaplun, and that said commission be authorized to create in the shortest time the most favourable conditions for the scientific work of Academician Pavlov and his collaborators;

2) the State Publishing House shall publish in a de-luxe edition, printed in the best printing shops of the Republic, the scientific works prepared by Academician Pavlov, summarizing the results of his scientific work for the last 20 years and that the property rights to that book both in Russia and abroad remain with Academician I. P. Pavlov;

3) the Workers' Food Administration shall furnish Academician Pavlov and his wife with a special ration equal in calories to two academic rations;

4) the Petrograd Soviet shall assure Professor Pavlov and his wife the lifelong use of the apartment occupied by them and furnish it and the laboratory of Academician Pavlov with the maximum of accommodations.

Chairman of the Council
of People's Commissars
V. Ulyanov (Lenin)

Moscow, Kremlin
January 24, 1921

And had you two lives, they would not have been enough. Science requires of an individual the utmost effort and a great passion. Be ardent in your work and in your quests."

Pavlov's love for science was not passive nor contemplative. Ivan Petrovich opposed the view of "science for its own sake." He always considered it as a powerful instrument for the solution of important applied problems. All his creative effort was bent on obtaining knowledge of the phenomena of nature in order to be able to govern them—to place science at the service of life. "To utilize nature's treasures and enjoy them," he said, "I must be healthy, strong and intelligent.... Physiology teaches us —more completely and more perfectly as time goes on—how to work, rest, eat, etc., correctly, i.e., with benefit and pleasure. But that is not all. It will teach us how correctly to think, feel and desire."

Considering it natural and useful that there be a close relationship between physiology and many aspects of applied activity as well as many theoretical subjects, such as psychology, pedagogy, etc., Pavlov was a particularly ardent supporter of the union between physiology and medicine. To this subject he devoted many colourful pages of his gifted scientific writings and several special lectures of brilliant form and content. He considered such a union to be of mutual benefit to both branches of learning, but especially to medicine. "The domain of pathological phenomena," he said, "is an infinite series of all kinds of *specific* combinations—i.e., such as do not occur in the normal course of life—of physiological phenomena. This is precisely, as if a series of physiological experiments were being carried out by nature and life. These are often such combinations of phenomena which would not for long have come to the minds of modern physiologists and certain of these combinations could not even have been reproduced intentionally by the technical means of modern physiology. Hence clinical case histories will always remain a rich source of new physiological ideas and unexpected physiological facts. It is therefore natural for a physiologist to desire a closer union between physiology and medicine."[1] Medicine needs this alliance still more; for in studying the complex phenomena of the human organism it employs almost exclusively the method of *observation*—a method both passive and very primitive, incapable of revealing the true nature of the processes occurring in a complex organism. For quite apparent reasons medicine cannot make use of *experiment,* the active and powerful instrument of modern science, which Pavlov employed in such an unexcelled masterful way in the domain of physiology. Medicine must, therefore, lean more and more heavily and to a wider extent on physiology and should make use in every possible way of all its valuable achievements. It must go through the "test of experiment." He wrote on this: "Observation is a method quite sufficient for the study of only the simpler phenomena. The more complicated a phenomenon is (and what is more complicated than life?) the greater is the need of experiment. Only experiment will crown the efforts of medicine, experiment limited only by the natural range of the human mind's creative powers.... *Observation collects that which nature has to offer, whereas experiment takes from her that which it desires. And the power of biological experiment is truly colossal.*"[2] (Italics mine.—*E.A.*)

Characteristic of Pavlov's correct understanding of the unity of theory and practice was that, in addition to his studies in pure physiology, themselves of enormous significance to medicine and other applied human activities, he made a number of special experimental investiga-

---

[1] I. P. Pavlov, *Complete Works*, Moscow-Leningrad 1946, Vol. II, p. 57.

[2] *Ibid.*, p. 357.

tions concerning the pathology and therapy of diseases of the heart and vascular system, of the digestive system, of the brain, etc. The trend of all Pavlov's scientific work is indicated by his statement: "An engineer finishes his studies of this or that machine by undergoing an examination which consists in assembling the entangled parts of the dismounted machine. This should also hold for a physiologist. *Only he can say that he has mastered the knowledge of life, who is able to return its disordered course to normal.*"[1] (Italics mine.—*E.A.*)

Pavlov considered one of the most important tasks of a physiologist to be the investigation of the origin, nature, and methods of treatment of the sick organism and that in time such investigations should form the basis of all the important branches of medicine. *"The more complete the experiments on animals will be, the less frequent will patients have to be in the position of experimental objects with all its sad consequences."*[2] (Italics mine.—*E. A.*) He became deeply convinced that only experiment will make medicine rational and its applications always and completely expedient. The great physiologist was of the opinion that: "In their fundamental sense physiology and medicine are inseparable. If the physician is actually, and even more ideally, an engineer of the human organism, then inevitably every new physiological discovery must sooner or later increase the physician's power over this extraordinary mechanism, his power to maintain and repair it."[3] Pavlov even considered it advisable to establish in medical schools three special departments of applied physiology, viz., normal, pathological and therapeutical.

---

[1] I. P. Pavlov, *Complete Works,* Vol. II, p. 354.

[2] *Ibid.*, p. 363.

[3] I. P. Pavlov, *Twenty Years of Objective Study of the Higher Nervous Activity (Behaviour) of Animals. Collection of Articles, Reports, Lectures and Addresses,* 6th edition, Moscow-Leningrad 1938, p. 78.

The knowledge that his scientific achievements were of a benefit to his beloved fatherland and that they heightened the authority of his native science was an unfailing source of inspiration for him during his long scientific career.

The great physiologist felt justly proud of the outstanding role played by our native physiology in many branches of that science and took sincere pleasure at every important contribution by our men of science to its treasury. He wrote to the Sechenov Society of Physiologists of Leningrad: "Yes, I am glad that, together with Ivan Mikhailovich (Sechenov), I and the group of my dear collaborators have won for the mighty realm of physiological research the whole and undivided animal organism instead of its vague half. And this is entirely our incontestable Russian contribution to world science, to human thought in general."

In Pavlov, the scientist, there was a harmonious union of unexcelled master of physiological experiment and great theoretician in biology, physiology and medicine.

He attached the greatest importance to the acquisition and accumulation of new data. Like Pisarev, he was of the opinion that "words and illusions perish—facts remain." He considered that only the verified and authentic "Mr. Fact" and nothing else has the last word in scientific controversies and in the study of the enigmas of nature. He himself always stood at the fountain head of dynamic science and was a most prolific acquirer of valuable scientific facts. He noted with satisfaction that: "... I always keep to the basis of facts; I check all my propositions by experiment and thus always find support in facts."[1] And in his "Letter to the Youth," which is a sort of scientific-literary self-portrait, this great toiler of science wrote: "Learn to do the hard, manual work in science. Study,

---

[1] I. P. Pavlov, *Twenty Years of Objective Study*, p. 187.

compare, and accumulate facts. No matter how perfect a bird's wing may be, it could never lift the bird to any height without the support of air. Facts are the air of a scientist. Without them you will never be able to fly, without them your 'theories' will only be vain attempts."[1]

Pavlov as experimenter possessed outstanding powers of observation. Not even the minutest details of the most involved experiments escaped his range of vision. He had the wonderful gift of finding new aspects of facts that may at first have appeared trite and insignificant, of interpreting them from a new point of view and finding a new meaning in them. This was a source of immense pleasure to him. He loved to experiment and would often remain for a long time in the soundproof chamber during the experiments of his collaborators, intently observing the behaviour of a dog.

In general, Pavlov attached the greatest importance to observation in research work and considered the ability to observe to be one of the chief virtues in a scientist. It is characteristic that at his request there were inscribed in large letters on the entrance to the laboratories of the scientific city at Koltushi the words: "Observation and observation."

But Pavlov was a stranger to crude and blind empiricism. He gave a prominent place to theory in scientific research, inculcated in every way among his collaborators a love for theory and regarded with contempt the "archivists" of facts. He considered a scientific theory necessary not only "that there be something to which facts can be connected" to explain them, but also "something with which to go forward." "If there are no ideas in our head, we shall not see the facts either," he said.

---

[1] I. P. Pavlov, *Complete Works,* Vol. I, Moscow-Leningrad 1940, p. 27.

"A real, legitimate scientific theory should not only embrace all the existing data, but also point out the way to further extensive studies and, if I may say, unlimited experimenting."[1] His attitude to theory was colourfully expressed, in particular, in his "Letter to the Youth." After the statement in that letter just cited (on the significance in scientific work of the accumulation of facts) he continued: "But when studying, experimenting, and observing, try not to remain at the surface of facts. Do not become archivists of facts. Try to penetrate into the secrets of their origin. Search persistently for the laws which govern them."[2]

As for Pavlov himself, he was and will remain forever one of the greatest theoreticians in science. The theories of the nervous regulation of the trophism (nutrition) of tissues and organs, of the activity of the chief digestive glands, and of the higher nervous activity, created by his genius, are an immortal, majestic monument to his scientific work, the lofty principles of which rested on the positions of militant materialism in natural science.

Pavlov exhibited outstanding integrity and courage in formulating and attacking scientific problems. His gift of scientific foresight was truly amazing and his novel ideas were of extensive scope and great depth. All this and his intuitive materialist-dialectic understanding of the phenomena of nature gave a mighty power to his experimental and theoretical work, a power to understand and to create, capable of eliminating any difficulties on the way to its goal. In his triumphant march of over 60 years along the road of science he solved many an intricate problem in biology and medicine in an easy and felicitous manner and many a secret of nature was unraveled by his genius.

---

[1] I P. Pavlov, *Twenty Years of Objective Study*, p 566.
[2] I. P. Pavlov, *Complete Works*, Vol. I, p. 27.

Finally, special mention should be made of the highly refined and superb style of Pavlov's creative work.

He was the most enthusiastic and most diligent of all his co-workers and did the manual work in the laboratory painstakingly and lovingly. He taught his pupils, above all, by personal example. Even at a very advanced age he continued to operate on animals, to experiment, and to participate personally in research work. He would follow with a vigilant eye the day-to-day research carried out by his numerous staff of collaborators, go into all the details of their investigations, and carefully check their experimental records.

Ivan Petrovich possessed the rare ability of welding his collaborators into a single, harmonious scientific unit. He organized the common work in an irreproachably precise manner. He achieved this not by formal, administrative measures, but by his noble qualities as a scholar and individual. He himself was always the heart and soul of his staff. "We are all harnessed to a common cause," he wrote, "and each pulls according to his strength and ability. Often it is impossible to discern what is 'mine' and what is 'yours' but our common cause only gains by this."[1] He considered that even the basic ideas in an investigation were—"the result of common endeavour, the result of the general 'atmosphere' in the laboratory to which every one is contributing something by himself and which all are absorbing."[2]

The scientific work of Ivan Petrovich was marked by an exceptional singleness of purpose. He never let his attention be scattered in different directions. When studying an important problem, he applied all his faculties and energy to it and put everything else aside for the time being. Even more—if in an involved problem his

---

[1] I. P. Pavlov, *Complete Works*, Vol. I, p. 28.

[2] *Ibid.*, Vol. II, p. 20.

attention was drawn to a single question, he would often temporarily lose active interest in all other aspects of that same problem. He was of the opinion that a scientist should be able to "persistently think of a single selected subject; to go to sleep with thoughts of it and to rise with thoughts of it." By thus focussing his activity to the utmost on a single subject, he was able, persistently and step by step, to achieve the solution of large and involved scientific problems. However, many important phenomena, which revealed themselves in the investigations, but were of little value in solving the problem under consideration, did not escape his keen eyes. He made no attempt to pursue these incidental facts at the time, but calmly stored them away in his unexcelled memory, to make them, at an opportune moment, the subject of separate investigation.

Before beginning the experimental solution of a scientific problem of any importance, Pavlov would carefully work out a detailed plan of attack and thoroughly discuss it with his collaborators. In that phase of the work, he was, as a rule, very attentive to the opinions, advice, and remarks of others and manifested considerable compliancy. But when putting his thoughts and ideas into practice, Ivan Petrovich waged a relentless offensive, casting no backward glance; an offensive which no difficulties, arising so frequently when complicated scientific problems are being solved, could stop. In this phase of the work, he did not always pay attention to the advice and remarks of his associates, especially if they came from sceptics and pessimists.

It never occurred to him to halt halfway and not bring his plans to a successful finish. This is well illustrated by the story of how he realized his idea of operating on the stomach to form a pouch, told by A. F. Samoilov in his memoirs. "I was a witness to the development of the stomach pouch operation," he wrote. "I remember how I was fascinated by Ivan Petrovich's courage and belief in the correctness of the plan he had worked out. At first the operation was unsuccessful. About 30 dogs had died in vain, a great deal of energy had been spent with no results, as well as a great deal of time—almost half a year. The faint-hearted were already beginning to lose confidence. I remember that certain professors in branches of science related to physiology asserted that the operation could not and would not succeed because the location of the blood vessels in the stomach made such an operation impossible. Ivan Petrovich laughed at such assertions as only he could laugh. A few more efforts and the operation began to be successful."

Pavlov's habit of checking every scientific fact over and over again and from all aspects also deserves special notice. He often varied the character of the experiments and used to check together the data of his collaborators. But, then, how highly he estimated those facts which withstood such a severe and critical trial, how he prized them, and how deeply he believed in them!

An important trait of Pavlov's scientific style of work was the exceptional scrupulousness and honesty with which he treated the history of the questions investigated and appraised the role played in their solution by his predecessors. He was very meticulous in his treatment of facts and conceptions held by other scientists. At the same time he was very exacting towards himself and extremely modest in evaluating his own contributions to science.

A daring revolutionary in science, he was at the same time very strict and careful about the publication of new data and new principles. At such times painful doubts did not leave him for a long time. Was he on the right path? Had everything been done to prevent errors? According to his wife, he very often could not fall asleep when tortured by such doubts before the publication of his most important scientific works. Thorough verification and analysis of new facts and also long and careful preliminary discussion of new principles together with his collaborators was an unalterable rule of his creative life. At these collective discussions, Pavlov's self-criticism often took on a censorious character. He would often appear as sarcastic opponent of his own "working hypotheses." In general he was a great lover of scientific discussions, an animated debater and put much youthful ardour and enthusiasm into his speeches. During these discussions he would not tolerate empty and idle talk by an opponent, nor would he countenance "rhetoricians," but was highly attentive to sound objections, especially if they were supported by facts. Such objections would even make him glad. He considered that they enabled him to approach involved scientific questions from different angles and either called forth new proofs for the defence of his point of view or enabled him to renounce erroneous conceptions. No matter how hard it may have been on occasion for Pavlov to part with his original views on this or that question, he did it ruthlessly and without hesitation, if convincing facts brought forward by his opponents or obtained by himself in the course of new experiments demanded it. He always placed scientific truth above all other considerations.

He was cautious to the utmost whenever the question arose of applying to human beings the conclusions arrived at in experiments on animals or applying the results of these experiments to the different aspects of medical practice. He always stressed the need for careful consideration of the specific features of the human organism.

In moulding the scientific characteristics of Pavlov's pupils, the chief role was played by his many-sided, charming personality, by the example of his own life and work, and by the process of his creative effort rather than by any method of pedagogical compulsion. His favourite expression was: "I like to teach by demonstration—not narration." And those who had the good fortune of becoming his pupils or collaborators not only tried to master this or that particular method of work, or the experimental technique of that virtuoso of physiological research; they acquired from him, continually, often without being aware of it, his ideas, the individual features of his creative work and the characteristics of his style in research.

But it would be a mistake to think that the process of educating and moulding new scientific personnel in the institutions under Pavlov's guidance was confined to a mere imitation of himself. Not at all! By characteristic methods Pavlov always directed the scientific growth of his pupils and their development according to their own inclinations, abilities, and other personal traits.

He unceasingly encouraged conscientiousness, assiduousness, initiative, and enthusiasm in his pupils and also their powers of observation. He would regularly make concrete remarks to all his students individually, on the character, direction, and nature of their scientific work, and of the data obtained, giving his views on the immediate and more remote objectives which followed from these results, etc.

He also had a number of individual ways of training his pupils in scientific methods.

It was highly significant to Pavlov's pupils that his attitude towards his co-workers was determined by their abilities and attitude towards work and by the theoretical and experimental results they obtained. He was not lavish in his praise and was more wont to "spur" them on. Nevertheless, one could detect, without much difficulty, various shades of difference in his attitude toward collaborators, depending on their scientific merits and each of them could quite easily and exactly determine Pavlov's attitude toward them.

Pavlov in every way encouraged independence among his collaborators. He not only did not hinder the scientifically mature pupils from becoming supervisors of scientific work in other institutions, but helped them to do so as much as possible, even if it excluded their working in institutes he directed.

And at last—a few words about Pavlov as a teacher in the strict sense of the word.

Ivan Petrovich possessed the rare gift of expressing his ideas, even on the most difficult subjects, in a concise, picturesque, and clear manner. According to the accounts of the older generations of his pupils, his lectures to the students of the Military Medical Academy were always a huge success.

"In the second year, when we began systematically to attend the lectures of Ivan Petrovich," recalled Academician L. A. Orbeli, "it became evident from his very first words that it would be impossible to miss any of his lectures, they were so lively and absorbing. They were characterized by an exceptional simplicity, an outstanding clarity and terseness in exposition and at the same time were very rich in content and were accompanied by very interesting experiments."

He preserved this gift of lively, colourful, and simple speech to the end of his days. Although he would say quite often that he liked to teach by demonstration and not narration, Pavlov talked willingly and always in a most fascinating way of the scientific problems in which he was interested, told of possible ways they could be attacked and in general on the perspectives of his scientific work. Perhaps one of the reasons for the organization of the weekly scientific meetings of the workers of Pavlov's laboratory (they took place on Wednesdays) was Ivan Petrovich's love for oral discourse and for work as pedagogue and lecturer. His talks on these "Wednesdays" were very often more like original lectures from which his pupils drew material for their scientific work.

Besides these meetings Pavlov's talent as pedagogue and conversationalist enabled his pupils to learn a great deal from every discourse with him. Such conversations always left an indelible impression on his collaborators and were rich sources of knowledge.

Pavlov's firmly established rules for scientific work and for educating young scientists, supported by immense experience, found vivid expression in his "Letter to the Youth."

This letter showed how infinite was Pavlov's love for our youth in general. The enthusiasm of the young was always a characteristic trait of his nature. This love for youth is symbolic too in that it characterizes Pavlov's optimistic views on the future of our country. He always looked upon youth as the future masters of our country, the builders of the new life which he had passionately acclaimed in his last years. He saw youth as his heirs in science, the continuers of the cause to which he had so devotedly dedicated the whole of his colourful, rich, and heroic life.

5. PAVLOV'S SCIENTIFIC WORK

"In the course of its development science has known not a few courageous men who were able to break down the old and create the new, despite all obstacles, despite everything."

J. V. STALIN

Pavlov was a scholar of manifold interests. His creative genius embraced diverse branches of physiology: blood circulation, digestion, secretion, the activity of the higher parts of the central nervous system, the neurohumoural regulation of the body functions, the physiology of work, comparative physiology, and also a number of problems in pharmacology, experimental pathology and therapeutics. But his most systematic and distinguished researches were conducted in three branches of physiology: blood circulation, the principal digestive glands, and the cerebral hemispheres. Here we shall give a brief summary of the very valuable facts he obtained and the theories derived from them.

But first—a few words on Pavlov's scientific method and on the fundamental principle guiding his research.

Pavlov's outstanding traits as a scientist found a vivid expression not only in his research work as such, but also in his method, one of the greatest achievements of modern natural science.

"For the naturalist, everything is in the method," he declared.

Prior to Pavlov, a largely one-sided analytical approach to the most complicated functions of the organism was prevalent in physiology in the form of the so-called vivisectional or "acute" experiment.

Following this method, the experimenter dissects in every possible way the body of an anaesthetized or, at times, unanaesthetized animal; he crudely destroys the intactness of the organism, uncovers the inner organs and may even wrench them from the body; he destroys the natural connections and interactions of the various parts of the organism and interferes with the normal course of its vital processes. And under such abnormal conditions, the scientist strives to shed light upon the laws governing the functions of the various organs and systems of the organism by stimulating, inhibiting, or blocking them with electrical, chemical, mechanical, thermal and other such artificial means!

Pavlov colourfully characterized the main shortcoming of this crude and hardly productive method, almost the only one employed by the early physiologists (and, regrettably, often used even at present) to study the higher manifestations of living nature. "We cannot calmly consent to the crude shattering of the mechanism," he wrote, "whose deep secrets have enthralled our minds for many years, perhaps even for a lifetime. If the mechanic often refuses to add anything to some delicate mechanism or change it in any way on the ground that it would be a pity to spoil it; if the artist reverently fears to touch his brush to the painting of some great master; then how can the physiologist abstain from such a feeling when he stands before the most delicate of all mechanisms, the unsurpassable masterpiece of living nature."[1] Among other reasons, Pavlov considered the vivisectional or acute method to be insufficient for acquiring knowledge of the laws governing the functions of this or that organ or system of the body, because "the usual method of

[1] I. P. Pavlov, *Vivisection. Complete Works*, Vol. V, 1949, p. 189.

simply dissecting the animal in an acute experiment involves, as it is now becoming clearer from day to day, a big source of errors, since the act of roughly interfering with the organism is accompanied by a mass of inhibitory influences on the functions of diverse organs."[1] Such an experiment is, therefore, unfit even "to obtain irreproachable analytical data," let alone synthetical, which, in general, can never be obtained in this way.

A virtuoso in the technique of vivisection (Sechenov considered Pavlov to be the best vivisectionist among European physiologists), Pavlov, nevertheless, was the first physiologist to make systematic use of the so-called chronic experiments, i.e., experiments made on unimpaired animals, or on such that had been operated on according to the strict rules of aseptical and anti-septical surgery (he was unexcelled also in such operations) and had recovered from the general effects of such operations. Such experiments facilitate analytical study of the functions of individual organs in many cases better than the "acute" method. But, what is more important, they afford the means for a thorough synthetic investigation of the most complicated functions of the organism. In other words, the experimenter can thus make a delicate, many-sided, and detailed study of the functions of the organs and systems of a healthy, unimpaired body in their normal relations and interactions. He can investigate the normal dynamics of physiological processes, disclose the laws governing the activity of organs and systems in their normal and undistorted aspect. He can "study the activity of the organism as a whole and of its parts in strictly normal conditions and in connection with these conditions."[2]

Highly skilled in the art of making a delicate, filigree analysis of the most complicated functions of the organ-

---

[1] I. P. Pavlov, *Complete Works,* Vol. II, p. 33.
[2] *Ibid.*, Vol. I, p. 363.

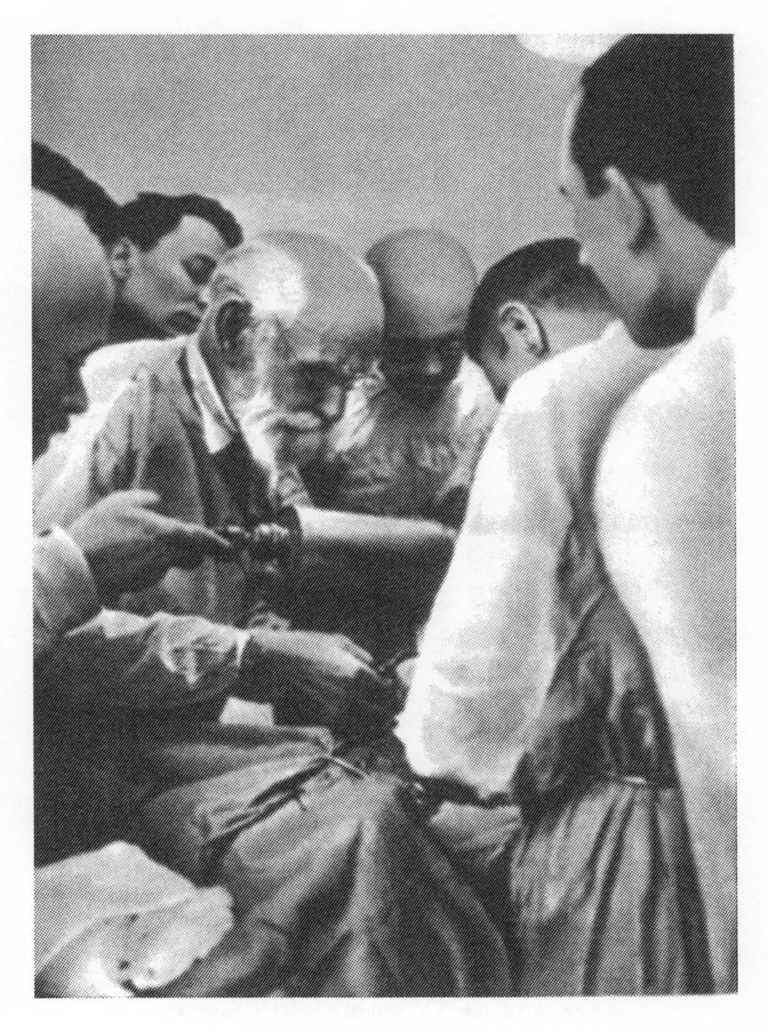

I. P. Pavlov operating

I. P. Pavlov speaking at the opening of the XV International Physiological Congress in 1935

I. P. Pavlov making a speech at a banquet in honour of the delegates of the XV International Congress

ism, he was the first in the world to begin their synthetic investigation; to be more exact, he supplemented the analytical approach to the functions of the organism with a synthetic one and thereby created a unified and essentially dialectical method of studying physiological laws. This is Pavlov's method, the most complete and most fruitful scientific method in physiology, which unceasingly furnished its creator with rich harvests of highly valuable facts in whatever branch of physiology he would apply his marvelous hands and keen and powerful mind.

Pavlov's method embodied the main features of his philosophy, his views on the integrity of the organism and on the unity of the organism and its environment. Such views associate him with the most eminent representatives of progressive Soviet biological science. "The animal organism," said Pavlov, "is an exceedingly intricate system, consisting of an almost infinite number of parts, connected both with one another and, in the form of a single complex, with surrounding nature with which it is in equilibrium."[1]

Pavlov by no means denied a certain contribution in our knowledge of this or that detail of the function of separate organs to the analytical method prevalent before his time. He wrote: "the object of analysis was to make the best possible acquaintance of the isolated part; that was its legitimate task; it determined the relationship of the part to the various phenomena of nature."[2] But that was insufficient. In spite of the usefulness of analysis in delicate physiological investigations, "the physiology of the organs was indeed greatly entangled by it." Hence it was necessary to pass over to a synthetic method of research, or rather, to supplement the analytical

---

[1] I. P. Pavlov, *Complete Works,* Vol. II, p. 452.
[2] *Ibid.*, Vol. I, p. 362.

method with a synthetic one and investigate the functions of the organism as a whole.

As we shall see, the beginnings of this celebrated method had already made their appearance in Pavlov's earliest researches on the physiology of blood circulation. More fully developed, it was responsible for the complete success of his studies on digestion and brought him world-wide recognition.

As if summarizing the results obtained on applying this method to digestion and foreseeing the bright perspectives it offered in the newly projected period of activity with its new, infinitely more complicated subject, Pavlov wrote:

"After a period of analytical work, we have entered without a single misgiving a synthetic period.... Judging from what we already know, synthesis, extensively applied to the whole organism as a new method, will be of great aid in the future physiological researches. It will become an energetic stimulant of other quests, of other investigations.... The object of synthesis is to determine the significance of each organ in its true aspect, from the standpoint of life; to ascertain its place and relative importance.... Synthesis is thus being carried out in two different types of physiological investigations. On the one hand, eager attempts are being made *to study the activity of the organism as a whole and in its parts under strictly normal conditions and in connection with these conditions* (Italics mine.—*E. A.*). As an example of this method, let me point out to the present work on the functions of the digestive glands. On the other hand we are putting forth and solving problems, the aim of which is to neutralize, to eliminate the harm done to the organism by any serious interference. Such is the case of the survival of vagotomized animals."[1]

---

[1] I. P. Pavlov, *Complete Works*, Vol. I, pp. 362-363.

Pavlov's method was continuously perfected during his investigations into the higher nervous activity. The importance of its composite parts—the analytical and synthetic approaches to the complex functions of the organism—was becoming more and more clearly defined. Defending the materialist theory of reflexes and his method against attacks by foreign psychologists of idealist views, Pavlov wrote in 1932:

"The organism consists of a great number of large parts and billions of cellular elements, which cause a corresponding number of respective separate phenomena that, however, are intimately connected with each other and together constitute the combined functioning of the organism. The theory of reflexes divides this general activity into separate ones, connecting them with internal as well as external influences, and then unites them together again. In this way the activity of the organism as a whole, as well as its interaction with its environment, is becoming more and more clarified."[1]

Pavlov's method reached its highest achievement in his studies of the brain, which unlocked the greatest of all nature's secrets and won him immortality.

No matter whether Pavlov had been studying blood circulation, digestion, the secretory organs, problems of comparative physiology or any other fields, all his investigations, regardless of how they may have differed in content or method, were always permeated by a single great idea: to investigate the nervous regulation of the activity of the organs and systems of the complex organism. This principle he fittingly termed neurism. "By neurism," wrote Pavlov, "I mean the tendency in physiology which tries to extend the influence of the nervous system on the greatest possible number of functions of the organism."[2]

---

[1] I. P. Pavlov, *Twenty Years of Objective Study*, p. 548.

[2] I P. Pavlov, *Complete Works*, Vol. I, p. 142.

An important role in the origin and development of Pavlov's fertile principle was played by the works of his predecessor in theory, I. M. Sechenov, also by his first teacher in physiology, I. F. Tsyon, and particularly, by the studies of the great Russian clinician, S. P. Botkin, whom Pavlov often met while working in the laboratory at the former's clinics. Pavlov wrote of this in his dissertation: "The idea of this investigation and its realization belong solely to me. But I was surrounded by the clinical ideas of Professor Botkin—and I acknowledge with heartfelt gratitude the fruitful influence on this work, and on my physiological views in general, of that profound and broad theory of 'neurism,' one that has often anticipated experimental data, and which, in my opinion, is Sergei Petrovich Botkin's chief contribution to physiology."[1]

It was due to "neurism," the lofty, fruitful principle wending its conspicuous way in the long years through Pavlov's scientific work, that he finally came to the physiology of the brain and it was there that this principle reached its acme.

* * *

To the study of blood circulation Pavlov devoted approximately the first fifteen years of his scientific career, chiefly during his work in the experimental laboratory at Botkin's clinics. His interest was then mainly fixed on two questions: the automatic regulation of blood circulatory organs by reflex action and the nature of the action of the efferent nerves on the heart.

The traits of Pavlov's original talent and the character of his future scientific method clearly appeared already in his first studies on blood circulation. Contrary to the unsuitable "acute" or vivisectional experiments then in general use for studying the reflex regulation of

[1] I. P. Pavlov, *Complete Works,* Vol. I, p 142.

blood circulation, Pavlov worked out and used for that purpose an entirely new physiological procedure which made it possible to eliminate completely the distorting effect of anaesthesia on the reflex actions of the nervous system, and, in particular, on the circulatory organs. By persistent training Pavlov accustomed the experimental dogs to lie on the operating table and calmly undergo without narcosis all the manipulations of an elaborate and lengthy experiment: incising the skin and subcutaneous tissues; disclosing the artery and connecting it to instruments for registering the blood pressure, etc. In these outstanding experiments Pavlov investigated the influence of food, feeding, and copious drinking on the arterial blood pressure and discovered a number of new, important laws concerning the spontaneous reflex regulation of the cardiac and vascular functions. Among other facts, he established, by these and by a series of other experiments, that not only a more or less significant rise in the arterial pressure but also its lowering can be rapidly and sensitively caught up by the sensory nerve endings in various parts of the vascular system. Owing to reflexes generated by the respective impulses from these signalizers, the work of the heart and the state of the vascular duct change in such a manner that the arterial pressure is quickly brought back to the original level and so remains comparatively constant.

Thus, there is a constant automatic regulation of the cardio-vascular function, and the arterial pressure is kept, as a rule, within certain average limits, the most favourable for supplying blood to the principal organs and systems of the organism. Pavlov also established that the sensitive "instruments" located in the walls of the blood vessels can detect changes not only in the blood pressure, but also in the chemical composition of the blood.

It should be pointed out that these and other facts disclosed by Pavlov and the conclusions drawn from them were of value to science not only in those far-off days, but they still retain an important place in our knowledge of the spontaneous reflex regulation of the organs of the circulatory system. Pavlov thus anticipated by about half a century the investigations of Göring, Heymans, Cordier, Koch, and many other contemporary foreign scientists engaged in the study of the specific receptory functions of the blood vessels and the automatic reflex regulation of the cardio-vascular activity. It should also be pointed out that Pavlov extended this principle, showing on the basis of other facts that not only the blood vessels, but all organs contain diverse specific sensitive devices adapted to respond to stimulants of a mechanical, physical, or chemical character. These devices play a very important role in the reflex regulation of many functions of the body. He wrote: "All organs and their tissues are permeated by these nerve endings. They should be conceived of as highly varied and specific, like the terminations of sensory nerves, each adapted to its own specific stimulant of a mechanical, physical or chemical origin. The degree of their activity at any given moment determines the magnitude and combinations of the activities of the organism."[1] These data and Pavlov's concepts are confirmed by the investigations of modern Soviet and foreign physiologists and have become one of the sources of a special approach in physiology, developed by his pupil K. M. Bykov—the systematic study of the receptory functions of the internal organs.

At that early period Pavlov gave much of his attention and time to the efferent cardiac nerves. Suffice it to say that his excellent doctoral thesis (1883) was devoted to this question. Hè found that among the efferent nerves of the heart there are some that can increase the force of the heart beat without increasing its frequency and others

[1] I. P. Pavlov, *Complete Works*, Vol I, p. 324.

that can change the frequency without changing its force. He further assumed that the efferent nerves have their antagonists—nerves that can weaken or slow down the contractions of the heart.

Later, Pavlov repeatedly returned to the question of the efferent cardiac nerves and carried out a number of new fundamental investigations on this subject. His attention was especially attracted to the nerves he had discovered which strengthen the heart beat. On the basis of careful experiments, Pavlov came to the entirely novel and highly important conclusion that these nerves augment the heart beat by heightening directly all the vital properties of the myocardium. Thereby was laid the basis for his future original, systematic, and profound theory of the existence of a special type of nervous influence on the tissues, the nervous trophic regulation (nutrition) of tissues and organs, an effect entirely different from the two others heretofore known to science (functional stimulation and regulation of the blood supply). One of the most eminent achievements of our native scientific thought, this theory, based on the highly valuable facts from the early period of Pavlov's scientific work as well as on new ones accumulated in the subsequent years, was presented in its finished form in a special report made by Pavlov in 1920. "Thus," said Pavlov in this report, "according to our conception, every organ should be under a ternary nervous control: the functional nerves, initiating or inhibiting its functional activity (muscular contraction, glandular secretion, etc.), the vascular nerves, regulating the bulk supply of chemical substances (and elimination of waste) by increasing or diminishing the blood supply to the organ, and, finally, the trophic nerves, determining, in the interests of the organism as a whole, the exact quantity of material to be ultimately utilized by each organ. Such a ternary control we have demonstrated in the case of the heart."[1] Further, Pavlov thought that the "chemical vital process" is regulated by trophic nerves in the tissues "according to a principle operating throughout the organism, in two opposite directions. Certain nerves strengthen this process and thus increase the vitality of the tissue, while others weaken the process, and if these latter are stimulated excessively, they will deprive the tissue of its ability to withstand the diverse destructive influences acting continuously inside and outside the organism."[2]

Among Pavlov's investigations on blood circulation still another study of a methodological character deserves attention. A great need had been felt in physiology and in other branches of experimental medicine and biology for a method of isolating the functioning heart of a mammal. By the 90's of the last century many outstanding scientists had been attacking this problem, but in vain. Pavlov also undertook its solution and did it in a number of ways. His ingenious method of isolating the functioning mammalian heart was developed in 1888. Published that same year, the method essentially amounts to replacing the systematic circulation by an artificial system of tubes whereas aeration of the circulating defibrinated blood is accomplished by the complete or partial preservation of the pulmonary circulation.

It should be mentioned that only ten years later did the English physiologist Starling succeed in developing a technique for isolating the functioning heart, quite similar to Pavlov's method both in idea and technical details. Bourgeois science, however, does not attribute the honour of this discovery to Pavlov, nor even to Pavlov and Starling together, but only to Starling alone. This is one of the many examples of the bourgeois falsification of

---

[1] I. P. Pavlov, *Complete Works,* Vol. I, p. 406.
[2] *Ibid.*, p. 403.

the history of science, one of the repugnant cases of the appropriation of the discoveries of our scientists by those in foreign countries. It is to be only regretted that there are also scientists in our country who are influenced by this erroneous conception.

Also of great value is another of Pavlov's methodological contributions, which too was carried out at this period of his career. This was an arrangement for studying on individual organs—the extremities, lungs, heart, etc.—changes in the peripheral blood circulation. Subsequently, Kravkov developed this line of work to a masterful degree of perfection.

Also to this period of Pavlov's efforts belongs one of his outstanding discoveries, which for decades anticipated the work of foreign scientists. Pavlov's acute sight had discerned a most interesting fact: blood in the cardio-vascular preparation did not clot for a long time although it was passing through a system of rubber and glass tubes, usually promoting its quick clotting. When, however, he had switched off the pulmonary circulation, coagulation set in quickly. On this basis, he, as early as 1877, concluded that an anti-coagulating agent was passing into the blood while it was circulating through the lungs. Pavlov's brilliant discovery was confirmed many years later; a powerful anti-coagulating agent, heparin, was isolated from the lung tissue.

* * *

Pavlov had worked on the digestive organs while yet in his student years at the university. After an interval of more than ten years he returned to this his first interest in science and applied himself assiduously to its development for about two more decades.

By their factual and theoretical results, the originality and skill of their execution, Pavlov's studies in the physiology of digestion are truly classical.

The study of digestion before Pavlov was one of the backward branches of physiology. Only very vague surmises had existed as to the laws governing the work of individual digestive glands and of the process of digestion as a whole. The vivisectional or "acute" experiment, the chief method in those times for investigating the functions of the digestive organs, was unable to get at their secret. More, the data obtained from such faulty experiments had become the sources of many errors; for instance, the view that the gastric and pancreatic glands were devoid of secretory nerves (Heidenhain, Starling, Bayliss, et al.). While some workers had been able by such experiments to establish the existence of secretory nerves in other digestive glands, for example, the salivary glands (Ludwig, Claude Bernard, Heidenhain, Langley, et al.), still, this crude experimental technique could not serve to bring to light all the intricate details of the nervous regulation of glandular functions.

Being aware of this, many scientists, both native and foreign (Claude Bernard, Heidenhain, Bassov, et al.), attempted to replace vivisection by more suitable chronic experiments on animals. Such attempts, however, did not meet with sufficient success. Either the operations performed were of little worth in concept and technique (Claude Bernard's fistula of the salivary ducts, Heidenhain's isolated stomach), or, though skilfully designed and successfully performed, were still insufficient to reveal the laws governing the work of the given organ (the gastric fistula of the dog proposed by Bassov).

Pavlov's genius led the physiology of the digestive organs out of its blind alley and raised it to unprecedented heights. And it was here, in the solution of this involved problem, that his celebrated method of the chronical physiological experiment was brought to its finished form.

The start was laid in new methods of physiological surgery of the alimentary canal, in the development of a new operational and experimental technique. "It is often said, and not without reason," declared Pavlov, "that science advances in leaps, depending upon the development of experimental methods. With every advance in method, we rise, so to say, one step higher and a wider horizon with heretofore imperceptible objects unfolds before us. Our first aim, therefore, was to develop a method."[1] And he devised and masterfully performed a series of ingenious and delicate operations—the formation of the stomach pouch, the division of the esophagus (esophagotomy) in combination with the stomach fistula, the pancreatic fistula, the salivary gland fistula, the terminal fistula of the bile duct, and other operations making more accessible for observation and experiment the internal digestive organs without impairing their innervation, blood supply, and the conditions of their life in general—that is, without disturbing their functions. (Incidentally we shall mention, in this connection, a highly interesting fact which does credit to our native science. In order to perform these operations according to the strict rules of human surgery, Pavlov was the first in the world to institute an operating room at the physiological laboratory similar to the operating rooms for human beings at surgical clinics.) After a post-operative period of several days the animals ordinarily recovered from the temporary general after-effects of the operation. Their health was restored and they differed in almost no way from the normal.

On such healthy animals with diverse chronic fistulas, "windows" in various parts of almost the whole digestive tract, Pavlov performed his studies on the physiology of digestion. It was thus possible to follow closely and

[1] I P. Pavlov, *Complete Works*, Vol. II, p. 23.

accurately the secretory activity of the digestive glands and collect pure digestive juices for study, as well as for therapeutic purposes in case of need. (At one time at the "gastric juice factory" in the Institute of Experimental Medicine 20 litres of pure gastric juice were being collected daily for therapeutic use.)

It should also be pointed out that the methods of investigating the fermentative, chemical, and physical properties of the various digestive juices in Pavlov's laboratory were for that time on a comparatively high level. Pavlov and his collaborators did not merely limit themselves to the available biochemical technique, but devised new methods which were then at a high state of perfection. Such, for example, was the method of "Mett tubes" for measuring the proteolytic strength of digestive juices.

Thus, by his accomplished and delicate technique of physiological surgery, the gifted naturalist paved the way for the realization of the fundamental principles of his method which allowed a much closer, detailed and all-sided study of the digestive glands to be made under normal conditions, without disturbing the processes taking place within them, in their undisturbed connection and coordination with the nervous, cardio-vascular, endocrine and other systems of the organism; without the "crude shattering" of the "delicate mechanism" and "masterpiece"—without disturbing the integrity of the complex organism.

"I consider the promotion of such an operational technique to be a matter of the greatest importance," wrote Pavlov, "because the usual method of simply incising the animal in an acute experiment involves, it is now becoming clearer from day to day, a big source of errors, since the act of roughly interfering with the organism is accompanied by a mass of inhibitory influences on the functions of the various organs. The organism as a whole, the result of the most delicate and most expedient connection of an enormous number of separate parts, cannot by the nature of the thing remain passive to destructive agents and must in its own interests strengthen one of the parts and weaken another; i.e., as if temporarily leaving aside all other aims, concentrate itself on saving that which can be saved. If this has been and still is a great obstacle in analytical physiology, then it appears to be an unsurmountable obstacle to the development of synthetic physiology where it is necessary to determine exactly the true course of this or that physiological phenomenon in the intact and normal organism."[1]

For about two decades Pavlov and his collaborators were engaged in an intensive study of the principal digestive glands. They investigated the effect on the glandular activity of the introduction of various amounts of different foods, of the smell and sight of food, and of diverse conditions of the organism and experiment. They examined how injury to the innervation affects the glandular activity, how physiological and pathogenic factors act upon the glands, etc.

These researches, performed by Pavlov with the elegance of a true artist of science, produced an unusual amount of new and valuable data and completely revolutionized the conceptions of physiologists and clinicians on the digestive process. They also served as the outgoing material for the development of Pavlov's theory on digestion. Pavlov gave convincing proof that the principal digestive glands (the gastric glands and pancreas) have a secretory innervation, i.e., nerves causing the secretion of digestive juices. This brilliant discovery immediately put an end to the then widespread misconception in physiology and medicine, connected with the names, in particular, of the English physiologists, Starling and Bayliss, of the absence of such innervation.

---

[1] I. P. Pavlov, *Complete Works*, Vol. II, p. 33.

For example, the nervous regulation of the gastric glands was demonstrated by Pavlov in the following exquisite experiment. The esophagus of a dog with a gastric fistula was severed at the dog's neck. Its ends were sutured to the edges of the skin wound at the neck, forming two openings. This is schematically shown on Fig. 1. After

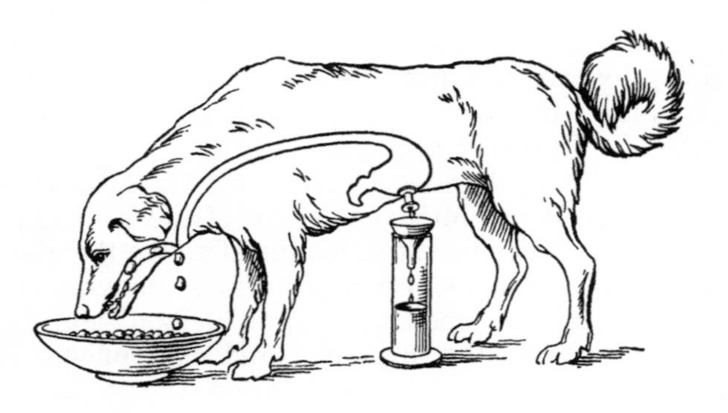

Fig. 1. Sham feeding of a dog with severed alimentary canal and stomach fistula

some time, when the dog completely recovered from the general effects of anaesthesia and of the operation and differed no longer from normal animals, a so-called "sham feeding" was organized. The dog was fed pieces of meat, bread or other food, but on being swallowed, the food did not reach the stomach, falling through the upper opening of the alimentary canal. This is also shown on Fig. 1. Several minutes after the start of the sham feeding, gastric juice begins to be secreted, quickly attaining considerable amounts, the secretion continuing for some minutes and even for hours.

Gastric secretion during sham feeding follows well-established physiological laws. But if the vagus nerves of the dog (nerves having their origin in the medulla oblongata and innervating with their ramifications, on descending, most of the inner organs of the thorax and the abdominal region, including the gastric glands) are severed, then sham feeding will no longer bring about the secretion of gastric juice. Pavlov's interpretation of this experiment bars all others. Essentially, it is as follows: the food stimulates the gustatory apparatus; the stimulation passes along the gustatory nerves to the medulla oblongata, whence by means of the vagus nerves it is transmitted to the gastric glands; i.e., in other words, a reflex is evoked from the oral cavity to the gastric glands. The severing of both vagus nerves interrupts the stimulatory wave in its way from the medulla oblongata to the gastric glands and the latter during the sham feeding remain inactive.

Subsequently, by analogous experiments, it was shown that the vagus nerves also contain secretory nerves for the pancreas.

It should be mentioned that long before Pavlov's experiments it had been known that branches of the vagus penetrate into the tissues of the stomach and pancreas. But the discredited technique of the "acute" experiment did not permit of indisputable proof that the nerve is related to the secretory functions of these digestive glands. In the ordinary "acute" experiment, the stimulation of the vagus by electric current or other means does not, in most cases, cause any noticeable secretion of gastric or pancreatic juices. For that reason, physiologists were of the opinion that the vagus is not a secretory nerve with respect to these glands, but one having vasco-motor and sensory functions. Pavlov's experiments corrected this error. They put physiology and therapy on the right path with respect to a very important theoretical and practical question.

In other experiments still more closely approaching the normal digestive process, Pavlov outstandingly brought to light the very intricate laws governing the

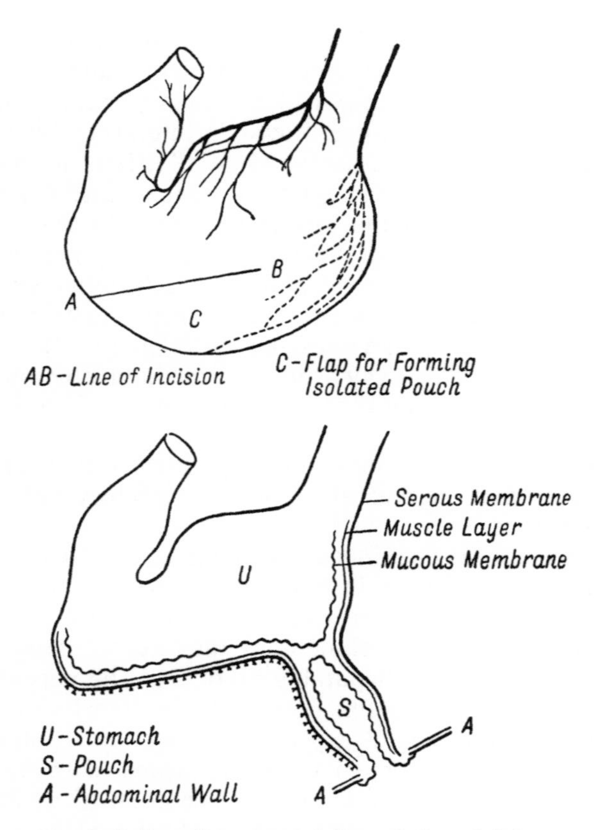

Fig. 2. Schematic representation of the miniature stomach operation (according to Pavlov)

nervous regulation of these and other digestive glands. He showed that, owing to the nervous regulation of glandular functions, the fermentative, chemical, and physical properties of the secreted digestive juices, as well as the dynamics of the secretion, adapt themselves very accurately to the quality and amount of food ingested and to the unpalatable substances introduced by the experimenter into any parts of the alimentary tract. For example, with respect to the gastric glands, this was demonstrated in the following way: the "sham feeding" experiment did not give a complete picture of the secretory function of the gastric and other glands. In such an experiment, food does not reach the stomach and therefore can exert no mechanical nor chemical action on its walls as it does during the normal digestive process. At the same time actual feeding of a dog with a gastric fistula could neither reveal the true dynamics of gastric secretion. The food and saliva entering the stomach greatly entangled the picture. To solve this problem, the German physiologist Heidenhain had attempted for a number of years to divide the stomach into two active parts functionally connected to one another. But his attempts were unsuccessful. Pavlov also applied himself to this difficult problem and after long and strenuous effort came to its brilliant solution. He performed the operation now known as the miniature stomach, or isolated gastric pouch. Without going into detail, we may say that this essentially amounts to cutting out a small pouch from the main part of the stomach, as can be seen from Fig. 2. The pouch is connected to the main part by common external walls and a common source of blood and nerve supply, but separated from it by an internal muscular wall. The cavities of the pouch as well as the stomach become accessible to the experimenter through fistulas. Food and saliva reaching the stomach do not enter the pouch because of the wall, but all that takes place in the glands of the stomach, as a result of the food reflex from the mouth or stomach or for other reasons, is exactly reproduced by the glands of the pouch. As Pavlov expressed it, all that occurs in the stomach is reflected as if by a mirror in the pouch.

Numerous experiments on dogs with stomach pouches showed that the amount and quality of the gastric juice secreted during actual feeding greatly depend not only on the amount of food consumed but also upon its kind. Fig. 3 depicts the secretion of gastric juice during the feeding of meat, bread and milk to the animal, and Fig. 4 the fluctuations in the digestive strength of the juice during that time. From the figures it can be seen that the maximum of secretion on ingestion of meat occurs at the

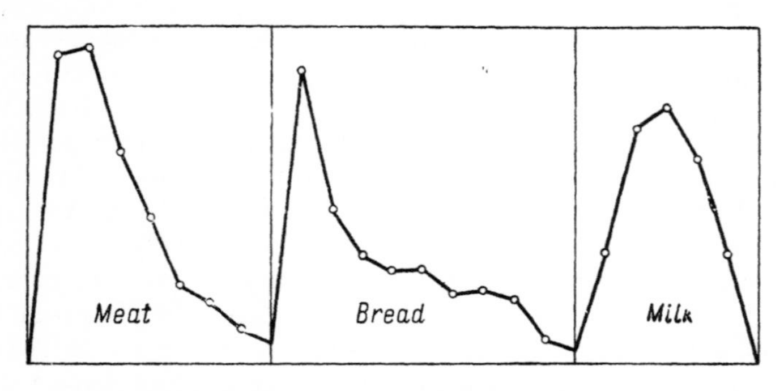

Fig. 3 Hourly fluctuations of the amounts of gastric juice secreted on eating meat, bread and milk (according to Pavlov). The abscissae represent hours and the ordinates, cubic centimetres

first or second hour, for bread, at the first hour, and for milk at the second or even the third. The duration of secretion is about 8 hours for meat, 10-12 for bread, and 5-6 for milk. As to the digestive strength of the juice, for meat it is highest in the first hour portion, for bread in the second and third hour portions and for milk in the very last hour portion. In other experiments Pavlov showed that the pancreas, the salivary and other digestive glands also very delicately adjust their activity and the character of the juice secreted to the amount, type, and quality of food. (See Fig. 5.)

He also established that the fermentative systems of the digestive juices can undergo considerable and stable adaptative changes, depending on the type of diet and its duration.

Pavlov discovered and investigated the so-called "psychical stimulation" of the digestive glands, i.e., the secretion caused by the animal's mere sight of food. This subsequently served as the starting point for his celebrated studies on the cerebral hemispheres. In complete harmony with his former data and conceptions on the existence of

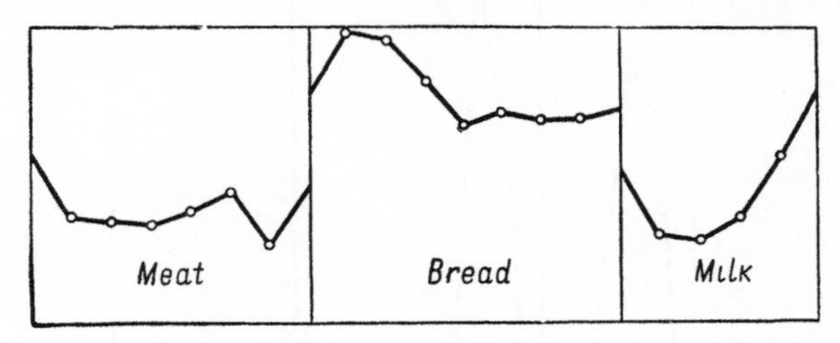

Fig 4 Hourly fluctuations of the proteolytic strength of gastric juice on eating meat, bread and milk (according to Pavlov)

a specialized sensory innervation in different parts of the vascular system as well as other internal organs, Pavlov demonstrated the existence of a very fine specific stimulation of the mucous membrane in various parts of the long alimentary tract. A great event in science was also the discovery of enterokinase by Pavlov and his collaborators, the first example of an "enzyme of enzymes" which laid the foundation for the discovery and investigation by other scientists of the extensive class of new biologically active substances known as "kinases" or "coenzymes." The two-sided action of enzymes was established. Factors were revealed which could stimulate or inhibit fermentative activity, increase or decrease the stability of the enzymes, etc.

It can be said without exaggeration that science owes its chief and most trustworthy information on the physiology of the digestive glands mostly to Pavlov. He virtually created anew this important branch of physiology, developed a monolithic, integrate theory of the digestive process in place of the former amorphous mass of vague, erroneous and unrelated data concerning the functions of

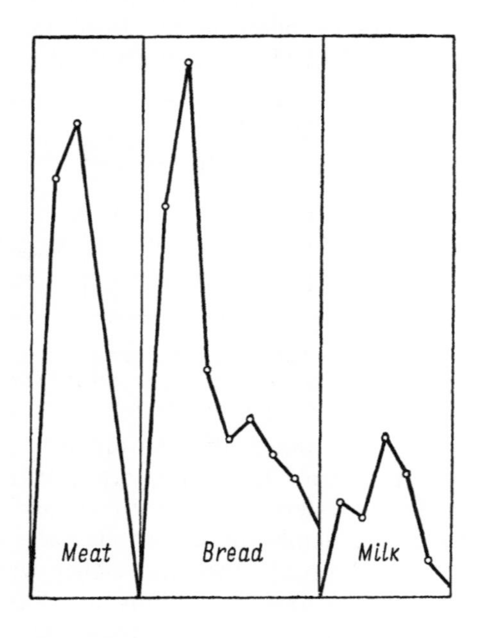

Fig 5. Hourly fluctuations of pancreatic juice on eating meat, bread and milk (according to Pavlov).

this or that organ of the digestive system. His classical studies on digestion laid a sound basis for subsequent researches by his pupils and followers in our country (V. V. Savich, I. P. Rasenkov, K. M. Bykov, U. V. Folbort, C. I. Chechulin, et al.) as well as abroad.

Pavlov made a brilliant comprehensive generalization of his experimental material and ideas in his classical book entitled *Work of the Digestive Glands* (1897) which was soon translated into the major European languages and brought him deserved renown throughout the world. He was the first among Russian scientists and the first in the world among physiologists to receive the Nobel Prize, awarded to him in 1904 for his work on the physiology of digestion. If it be borne in mind that the Nobel Prize jury does not in general confer the award very willingly to Russians although there always were and are not a few first-class scientists in our country, the awarding of this prize to Pavlov should be considered as proof of the exceptionally high estimation of his scientific merits by the progressive scientists of the world, which could no longer be ignored.

In the course of these investigations, Pavlov had collected a large number of facts dealing with the trophic innervation of tissues. This material together with the analogous facts he had obtained concerning blood circulation served as the foundation upon which he built his theory of trophic innervation. In that same period of his experimental studies, Pavlov devoted a great deal of attention to experimental pathology and gastrotherapy, laying the foundation for this important branch of medicine.

Many years later, while in the very midst of his studies on the higher nervous activity, an occasion was presented to him to cast a bird's-eye view on his work on the physiology of digestion. And he had full reason to "look back with satisfaction" on his glorious path and say: "During that time, our methods, our basic ideas on that subject, our general and even detailed characterization of the work of the glands, and almost every one of our separate facts have found an almost general application, recognition, confirmation and further development in numerous investigations in clinics and laboratories by both native and foreign authors."[1]

These words are valid now and will be in the future. Time is powerless to depreciate such masterpieces of science.

* * *

We have already said that all of Pavlov's work was permeated by a single great principle which he called "neurism." This principle logically brought the great naturalist to the physiology of the brain. It reached its culmination in the study of this "headquarters" of the nervous system.

Pavlov turned to cerebral physiology on the threshold of the 20th century and continued working in that field to the end of his days. In the course of 35 years of intense work his genius produced the materialist conception of the higher nervous activity, the crowning point of his scientific endeavours and one of the greatest achievements of science both at home and abroad.

Prior to Pavlov, the perseverant efforts of many scientists of the 18th and especially the 19th centuries had already established that mental activity is a function of the higher parts of the central nervous system. A long, zigzag and thorny path in physiology had been overcome, and the inquisitive mind of man had from the naive surmises of the ancient Greek philosophers reached the strict factual proof of this cardinal truth, the basis of natural science and materialism.

The physiological methods extensively used in former times to study the brain consisted of extirpation and stimulation under conditions of crude vivisection. Scientists armed with facts obtained by their aid could at best only define and give a superficial description of the part played

---

[1] I. P. Pavlov, *Complete Works*, Vol. II, p. 18.

by the brain in the lower and higher vertebrates. They could only make general surmises as to the localization of functions in various parts of the cerebral hemispheres (particularly the cerebral cortex). The situation was no better in the other branches of science dealing with the brain. Other biological and clinical methods added nothing of any significance to this rather dreary picture. The noted German physiologist Goltz, who contributed more than any other of his contemporaries to the experimental study of the functions of the brain, truly characterized the then prevailing state of affairs. After about 30 years of strenuous effort he was forced to sadly complain: "... anyone who has been engaged in fundamentally studying the physiology of the cerebrum will agree with me that we have little more indubitable knowledge of the processes occurring in this primary organ than we have of Mars."[1]

Cerebral physiology had been making no headway in the 19th century. The role played by the brain in animals standing on various levels of the evolutionary scale including dogs and even apes had been ascertained in a most general manner. But no way was known how to investigate this role, how to study the laws governing the cerebral activity, how to ascertain what processes form the basis of the latter, their nature and occurrence—in other words, there was no knowledge of the genuine physiology of the brain. True, the view that the brain functions by means of reflexes had been rather widespread among the more advanced biologists and physiologists of that time (Sechenov, Griesinger, Darwin, Huxley, et al.). But this conception, however original and progressive it may have been, had yet been unable not only to bring cerebral physiology out of the cul-de-sac in which it had found itself but even to prevent the crisis in method

[1] F. Goltz, *Verhandlungen des Kongresses für Innere Medizin*, 1884, p. 262

from becoming a crisis in methodology. At that time such a conception was necessarily of a speculative character. It had no direct nor sound experimental proof. Physiologists studying the functions of the brain were in a state of perplexity. Pavlov in one of his early discussions on that subject declared regretfully that "... the physiology of the higher parts of the brain is now at a complete standstill"; that it has received "very few new ideas." "One can truly say," he wrote, "that the irresistible progress of natural science since the time of Galileo has halted perceptibly for the first time before the study of the higher parts of the brain, the organ of the most complicated relationship between animals and the external world. And this apparently was not without reason. Here indeed was the critical moment of natural science. For the cerebrum, which in its highest form—the human brain—created and is continuing to create natural science, itself became an object of this science."[1]

About that time, in a polemic with the well-known scientist, V. M. Bekhterev, Pavlov stated: "Yes, at the last meeting I said that beginning with the 70's the physiology of the cerebrum has made no progress, that nothing new has been done in this field for the past 30 years. Of course, the elaboration of insignificant details has been taking place, but the guiding ideas, the fundamental methods had been exhausted in the 70's. Thereafter they have only been applied to details and broadened. But this is only imitation and not true creative work. As for anything new, nothing has been done these 30 years, all is marking time within the old framework."[2]

It goes without saying that this lack of progress in the study of the functions of the cerebrum played into the hands of reactionaries. Driven out of many scientific fields they had found refuge in the idealist psychology and

[1] I. P. Pavlov, *Twenty Years of Objective Study,* p. 111.

[2] I P. Pavlov, *Complete Works,* Vol. I, p. 392.

zoopsychology of the time. All possible kinds of idealist conceptions of psychical activity and of the "soul" as a certain mystical supernatural principle developed rapidly.

This is briefly the prehistory of Pavlov's theory of the higher nervous activity.

With such a dark picture as the background, especially brilliant stands out the scientific feat of Pavlov, who brought this most important field of natural science out of its blind alley on to the broad highway of progress But, of course, this should not give ground for underestimating the highly important experimental and theoretical work of Pavlov's nearest and even remote predecessors. Particular mention should be made of Sechenov. It was he whom Pavlov considered to be his ideological forerunner and whose profound ideas favoured the birth and quick development of Pavlov's new theory. Pavlov himself wrote about this as follows: "... the chief impetus to my decision (although I had not been conscious of it at that time) was given by the talented booklet of Ivan Mikhailovich Sechenov, the father of Russian physiology, entitled *Reflexes of the Brain,* the influence of which I had felt when still a youth."

Thus, on the border of the two centuries, there had already, to put it in Pavlov's own words, "... arisen a need to pass over to the experimental analysis of the subject, an analysis from the same objective, external standpoint as in the other branches of natural science."

And this he did resolutely, bravely and splendidly.

Also highly instructive is the history of Pavlov's transition from the physiology of digestion to the physiology of the brain. This transition was the direct result of, and even spurred on by, an interesting phenomenon in the activity of certain digestive glands. Pavlov had first observed this phenomenon as far back as the beginning of the 1890's when studying gastric secretion. He and his collaborators discovered that gastric juice was secreted by dogs not only on being fed or during "sham feeding" but also at the mere sight of food. At that time, entirely absorbed by the study of the physiology of digestion as such, Pavlov decided to postpone a detailed investigation of this highly interesting "psychical stimulation" of the gastric glands. Strange as it may seem, he even satisfied himself with an essentially idealist interpretation of it from the standpoint of subjective psychology: the dog is hungry or is thinking of food and is therefore secreting juice. It can hardly be said that Pavlov's conception of the psychical secretion of gastric juice suffered any essential change by his remark that here "the excitation of the nerves of the gastric glands was due to a psychical factor which had assumed a physiological character." That ". . . on considering all phenomena from a purely physiological standpoint, this can be called a complicated reflex act," etc. Ivan Petrovich was then of the opinion that this was the result of the fact that food ". . . must be acquired not only by muscular effort but also by the aid of higher functions—the animal's judgment, will and desires."[1]

Pavlov again met with this same phenomenon after several years, this time while studying the salivary glands. Dogs salivated at the sight of test tubes which had been used for pouring mild acid solutions into their mouths. He considered this at first in the same subjective psychological light as the "psychical secretion" of gastric juice and gave it a psychological term, "speaking very freely and with much heat of the thoughts, desires and feelings of the experimental animals,"—he himself ironically said later. But this interesting "psychical stimulation" of the salivary glands let itself be felt so often in the everyday work of Pavlov and his collaborators that it

---

[1] I. P. Pavlov, *Lectures on the Work of the Principal Digestive Glands*, 1949, p. 105.

became a serious obstacle in their studies. He could, therefore "... no longer postpone the investigation of these phenomena." More than that, he could not overcome an ever-increasing doubt as to his correctness in considering these phenomena from the subjective-psychological point of view.

His attention and the main point of his research were imperceptibly being transferred to a new and highly in-

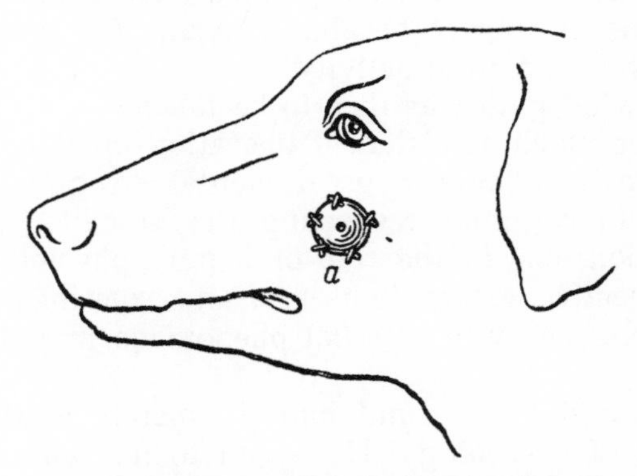

Fig. 6. Fistula of the parotid salivary duct in a dog

teresting field of biology. He became more and more engrossed with the nature, "mechanism," and source of the "psychical stimulation" of the gastric glands and with the question of how to investigate these and similar phenomena of the wonderfully delicate and exact adaptation of the organism to the quickly changing conditions of existence.

Pavlov became more and more convinced of the "absurdity and futility" of his attempts to penetrate into the inner world of animals and to make any conjectures, like the zoopsychologists, as to their moods, desires, inclinations, and feelings. He saw the uselessness of his attempts to throw light on the subjective world of animals through the prism of the subjective world of man and to interpret the nature of the phenomena observed by anthropomorphic comparisons. The "psychical stimulation" of the salivary glands ("the mouth waters") had been known with respect to man from time immemorial. Even as far back as in the middle of the 18th century it had attracted the attention of Witte and other scientists. Still, it was never really explained from a psychological viewpoint and never became a means for grasping the more complex mental activity.

But what path was then to be taken?

"After much persistent deliberation on that subject," wrote Pavlov, "after a great mental struggle, I finally decided to continue respecting the so-called psychical stimulation also in the role of a pure physiologist, i.e., of an objective, external observer and experimenter, dealing exclusively with external phenomena and their relations."[1]

Pavlov did not limit himself merely to the placid rejection of psychology. He began to feel an irreconcilable hostility to this false "ally of physiology."

Pavlov's rejection of psychology was no doubt influenced by his outlook. Being a confirmed materialist he considered that the psychology of that time, still entirely permeated by idealism, had not attained the status of an exact science and possessed no clear, well-defined theoretical basis, nor any definite method of research.*

---

[1] I. P. Pavlov, *Twenty Years of Objective Study*, p. 13.

* Pavlov did not significantly alter his strongly negative attitude to psychology for a long time, although considerable changes had been taking place in that field. As far back as in the 1890's there had appeared and developed quite rapidly an essentially materialist trend in comparative psychology seeking to investigate animal behaviour by as objective a procedure as possible (Lubbock, Morgan, Thorndyke, Loeb, Beer, Bethé, Uexküll, et al.). When he

He considered it, therefore, erroneous and quite absurd for a physiologist-materialist to seek the aid of this "science" in solving the highly involved questions of nervous activity. It was an inexcusable mistake of scientists "that natural science, as represented by the physiologist studying the higher parts of the central nervous system, should, unconsciously, so to say, without noticing it, come under the sway of a current fashion—that of considering the complex behaviour of animals by comparing them with ourselves, accepting the same inner causes of their actions as those which we feel and recognize in ourselves."[1]

More than that, Pavlov considered that the reason why no progress was being made in the physiology of the brain was just because "the physiologist had left at that point the sound position of natural science" in favour of the "fantastical and scientifically barren position" of subjective psychology. This led him to the logical conclusion that: "In view of such a state of affairs, common sense demands that physiology should return here also to the way of natural science. What then must it do? It must remain true to the same methods in studying the activity of the higher parts of the central nervous system as those which it employed in studying the lower parts, i.e., it must make an exact correlation between changes in the external world and the respective changes in the animal organism, and discover the laws governing these relations."[2]

Thus, in order to bring to light the deepest secrets of the function of the cerebral hemispheres, the highest and most perfect creation of living nature, "purely physiologi-

---

learned of that later, Pavlov did not hesitate to accord the pioneers in this movement due merit and proper appraisal of their work.

[1] I. P. Pavlov, *Twenty Years of Objective Study*, p. 112.

[2] *Ibid.*, p. 113.

cally, purely materialistically and purely spatially," Pavlov resolutely set out on the tried path of the naturalist, the path of exact experiment, objective observation, and strict reasoning because "... investigation thus always rests on a sound basis of material facts similar to the other fields of natural science. Owing to this, exact material is being gathered ceaselessly and the horizons of research are being tremendously widened."[1]

First of all Pavlov reconsidered from the new positions the ill-starred "psychical salivation." He fully demonstrated, without much difficulty, that this phenomenon possesses all the fundamental characteristics of a reflex act, i.e., the reaction of the organism to stimulation of any one of its parts through the nervous system. Indeed, if the sight of food or a test tube with acid causes secretion of a dog's salivary glands in just the same way as if food or acid had been introduced into its mouth, then there was no ground for not calling the reaction of the salivary glands to the sight of food or test tube a reflex act.

But Pavlov was very quick to ascertain that this was a special type of reflex act, significantly differing in many ways from the reflexes earlier known to physiology. In particular, he established that it was greatly dependent on the experimental conditions and, in general, on the conditions of existence of the animal. For that reason he called it a conditioned reflex. To the other, earlier known, reflexes he gave the name unconditioned.

It may appear, at first sight, that there is nothing much to renaming "psychical stimulation" by "conditioned reflex." Did not Sechenov, Griesinger, Huxley, et al., long before Pavlov, hold that mental activity can be traced to complex reflexes, to "reflexes of the brain"?

But in reality that which Pavlov did was entirely novel.

---

[1] I. P. Pavlov, *Twenty Years of Objective Study*, p 282.

Sechenov and other advanced natural scientists of the middle and end of the 19th century had ingeniously employed the "cerebral reflexes" for developing progressive outlines and concepts. They converted this into a sharp instrument for their highly useful theoretical writings. They used them in their passionate and very successful polemics against representatives of reactionary trends in psychology. This was their great contribution to science. But their ideas as to the reflex character of the mental activity of animals and man, daring, progressive, and attractive as they had been, still were abstract and contemplative. They had the nature, in Pavlov's words, of "physiological schemes" and were therefore devoid of an effective power. They were far from being a scientific method. It is characteristic that in the nearly half a century of their existence, these conceptions had found almost no significant reflection in the current experimental work on cerebral physiology, neither in our country nor abroad.

All the above to a considerable degree refers also to the most eminent, profound, and consistent of these progressive thinkers, I. M. Sechenov, the founder of the cerebral reflex theory, which to Pavlov was an "ingenious flight of Russian thought." Sechenov's famous booklet *Reflexes of the Brain* was published in 1863 and in it, according to Pavlov, "a brilliant attempt was made, truly extraordinary for that time (of course only theoretically, as a physiological outline), to represent our subjective world in a purely physiological aspect."[1] "In a clear, precise, and charming form," continued Pavlov, "this booklet contained the fundamentals which are now developing." Pavlov held that Sechenov's extending the conception of the reflex act to include the higher nervous activity was a true feat for those times and that this bold

[1] I. P. Pavlov, *Twenty Years of Objective Study*, p 13.

idea had become "a scientific force for directing the immense contemporary work upon the brain"; but still, "all this was mere conjecture," devoid of the solid foundation of tangible scientific facts.

What Pavlov did was entirely different in principle.

Pavlov, above all, used his "conditioned reflex" as a tool for actual work, for experimenting, for acquiring precise data. He soon firmly established that the conditioned reflex is the most typical form of cerebral function and the basic link in the chain of its complicated laws. The phenomenon of "the mouth waters," known from time immemorial, but not understood nor appreciated by scientists for hundreds of years, became of great significance in the light of Pavlov's materialist interpretation. It opened broad horizons for investigating the physiology of the brain, becoming the basis upon which new principles were built for studying the cerebral activity, the basis of the method of conditioned reflexes.*

Pavlov's new method and the novel experimental technique for studying the brain arising from it were related in principle to his method and partly to the procedures he used for studying the digestive glands. In fact, it was his famous synthetic method developed to the highest perfection. Here also the studies were made upon animals (usually dogs) under normal conditions. The processes of the organ under investigation, in this case the brain, were studied in its natural connections and interactions with the other parts of the central nervous system and the

* It is just this highly important circumstance which the reactionary foreign scientists (Fulton et al.) lose sight of when they strive to belittle the significance of Pavlov's immortal materialist theory of the higher nervous activity by bombastic statements to the effect that Sherrington, Meinert, Twitmayer, or some other scientist had already observed phenomena of the conditioned reflex type before Pavlov. In addition to everything else, these attempts show that such "critics" of Pavlov simply do not understand the nature of what they undertake to judge.

I. P. Pavlov during an operation

Demonstration of an experiment during a lecture by I. P. Pavlov to the students of the Military Medical Academy

A cross section of the chamber for studying conditioned reflexes. On the left—the interior part of the chamber; on the right, the exterior part

organism in general, i.e., the researches were made under conditions of the normal functioning of the animal. There was an insignificant element of artificiality only in the isolation of the animal in a special room or box during the experiment and in placing it on an experimental table, on which, however, it could stand, sit and even move about within certain limits. This could not essentially influence the natural course of the processes in its organism, including those in the nervous system. Most animals quickly and easily became accustomed to the experimental conditions.

At first the conditions under which Pavlov and his collaborators studied the physiology of the brain were still less artificial, although more primitive. The experimenter remained alongside the animal and himself made all the manipulations (fed the dog, poured the acid solution into its mouth, showed it the food or test tube, made observations and records of the process of salivation, etc.). But soon it became apparent that the salivary reflex was evoked not only by the sight of food or test tube, but by other, chance stimuli not related to the functioning of the salivary glands (auditory, visual, olfactory, mechanical irritation of the skin, etc.), intentionally or accidentally associated for a number of times with feeding or the pouring of acid into the mouth, and it became necessary to isolate the animal more or less from the experimenter, other people, and casual articles. Subsequently, the experimental animals were placed in special thick-walled "conditioned reflex boxes" which could completely isolate the experimenter and thus eliminate the possible unexpected action of any extraneous stimulus which might have distorted the picture of the cerebral activity and hampered its study. At the same time, the experimenter by the aid of special devices could see and hear the animal, apply this or that stimulus in the box, produce conditioned or unconditioned food, defence, or other reflex actions, accurately and objectively determine their quantitative or qualitative peculiarities, etc.

Thus Pavlov set forth to revolutionize research in this most difficult biological field both in principle and in method. The venerable naturalist, with years behind him of successful fathoming other secrets of living nature, began the unveiling of this most complicated of her riddles. And his long strenuous endeavour was rewarded with triumph.

What then were the new facts obtained by Pavlov and his pupils; how were they interpreted; and what is the essence of his theory of the higher nervous activity?

For many years his attention and that of his collaborators had been directed to investigating in all their aspects the specific features of the conditioned reflex, the peculiar functional unit, the chief and most characteristic form of cerebral activity on which ultimately rests the entire higher nervous activity, almost the entire behaviour of highly developed organisms. "The central physiological phenomenon in the normal work of the cerebral hemispheres," wrote Pavlov, "is that which we have called the *conditioned reflex*. This is the temporary nervous connection between the innumerable agents of the environment of the animal, acting on its receptors, and definite actions of the organism."[1]

The detailed and multifarious study of the peculiarities of this new type of reflex laid the granite foundation for the new theory.

It was established by accurate data that conditioned reflexes in contradistinction to the unconditioned are not inborn forms of nervous activity nor transmitted by inheritance in the ordinary sense of the word, but are *developed in the course of the individuum's own life*. Pavlov most often illustrated the correctness of this statement by the following facts: pups were raised up to a

---

[1] I P. Pavlov, *Twenty Years of Objective Study*, p. 603

certain age on a milk diet only. Special experiments showed that the mere sight of milk was able to evoke in them the salivary reflex, whereas the sight of other food of which they as yet had had no acquaintance, such as meat or bread, did not induce salivation. But the pups needed to be fed only once or twice with bread or meat for the mere sight of that food to produce the so-called natural salivary food reflex.

Leaving aside for the moment Pavlov's views on the possibility of a hereditary fixation of the conditioned reflex, we point to one of the most important principles of his theory: viz., *the physiological basis upon which a conditioned or acquired reflex is formed is an unconditioned or inborn reflex.* That this is so is very convincingly demonstrated by the development of artificial salivary reflexes, i.e., conditioned reflexes to the most varied stimuli having nothing whatever to do with food, nor bearing any relation to the digestive glands, for example, reflexes to the lighting of an electric lamp, ringing of a bell, ticking of a metronome, to the touching of the skin of the animal, etc. In order to convert any one of these stimuli (let us say the lighting of a lamp) into a conditioned stimulus evoking salivation it is necessary to combine the feeding of the animal repeatedly with the lighting of a lamp. Thereafter this action alone will cause the same secretion of saliva as the food itself, i.e., it becomes, so to say, a substitute for the food or a signal of it. In just the same way any other stimuli bearing no relation to nutrition can be transformed into conditioned stimuli or signals, if only they are perceived by any one of the sense organs or even by the sensory nerves of the muscles, joints or internal organs.

New conditioned reflexes can be developed not only directly on the basis of an unconditioned reflex, but on an already acquired strong and stable conditioned one. To do this, a not too strong extraneous stimulus is coupled in a special way with the conditioned reflex already present. The newly developed reflex is called a conditioned reflex of the second order. Very often a third order reflex can be developed in such a way. It is not difficult to see that these conditioned reflexes of higher order are also ultimately based on the respective unconditioned one.

The association of the extraneous stimulus with an unconditioned reflex is necessary not only for the formation of conditioned reflexes but also for their preservation. If this fundamental condition is in any way not fulfilled, then even old and strong conditioned reflexes gradually weaken and disappear. This, for example, takes place if food is shown several times in succession to a dog but is not given to it, or when the artificial food reflex signal (in our example—the light) is repeated for many times in several intervals, but not reinforced by food, etc. These and similar data bear witness to *one of the most important and most characteristic properties of the conditioned reflex—its temporary nature. "We can rightly call,"* wrote Pavlov, *"the permanent connection between an external agent and the response of the organism it evokes an unconditioned reflex while the temporary connection can be called a conditioned reflex."*[1]

It is interesting that the disappearance of a conditioned reflex is in its turn of a temporary character. In some cases it is re-established spontaneously, some time after its disappearance, while, in others, one must have recourse anew to repeated associations of the conditioned stimulus with the unconditioned reflex or to other procedures.

The dependence of the conditioned reflexes on their association with unconditioned ones determines, if not quite completely, yet sufficiently clearly, another important property, their exceptional fragility, their utmost variability. Conditioned reflexes depend infinitely more than

---

[1] I. P. Pavlov, *Twenty Years of Objective Study*, p. 710.

unconditioned ones on the state of existence of the animal both in and outside of the laboratory, on its health, its care, on changes in the accustomed experimental conditions, etc. Under the influence of each of these factors separately, or in combination, the conditioned reflexes may, at times slowly, at other times quickly, grow feeble or disappear altogether for greater or smaller periods of time. Pavlov considered that it is "*the extraordinary dependence of the new kind of reflex* both on the phenomena within the organism and on its surroundings" which *characterizes it more vividly than all the other properties* which we have already described. That is why he preferred the term conditioned reflex to all others such as individual, associate, temporary, connective, etc.

The conditioned reflex differs from the unconditioned one by yet two other closely related properties. Each unconditioned reflex is evoked by a comparatively small number of specific, or, as they are called, adequate, stimuli and only when they act on a certain one of the sense organs, on a definite area of the skin or on some internal organ (the law of the receptor field). For example, the unconditioned food-salivary reflex can be evoked only by food and then only when it is in the mouth. The conditioned reflex has no such limitations. To produce it *no adequate stimulus nor specific receptor field for the latter's application* are needed. Any stimulus capable of exciting any external or internal sense organs may become a conditioned food stimulus and consequently elicit salivary secretion. Moreover, a conditioned reflex can be developed not only to individual stimuli, perceptible to an external sense organ, or to the sensory elements of the muscles, tendons, joints, or internal organs, but also to combinations of two, three, or more, different stimuli applied simultaneously or in sequence followed by the reinforcement of an unconditioned reflex. Such conditioned reflexes are called complex. Furthermore, the conditioned stimulus may be the lapse of time. If, for example, food is given to a dog every five minutes without being accompanied by any stimulating agents, then, in time, salivation will occur after each feeding on approaching the end of the interval. A conditioned reflex may also be established to the order in which a stimulus is applied, to the discontinuance of its action, to the ratio between stimuli, in a word, to any changes in the environment or within the animal, if only they are perceived by a sense organ or directly by the nervous system. Pavlov formulated this basic principle as follows: *"The infinite fluctuations in both the outer and inner mediums of the organism, each of which is reflected in definite states of the nervous cells of the cerebral cortex, may become separate conditioned stimuli."*[1]

In Pavlov's laboratories the activity of the salivary gland was employed as the main indicator for studying the conditioned reflex behaviour of animals. This was not so much a matter of tradition as of the fact that the salivary gland, because of its modest role in the organism, the small number of its connections with other organs and systems, the simplicity of the laws governing its action, the ease and convenience of its measurement (by a chronic fistula in the salivary duct), and other such properties, proved to be a very sensitive, accurate and adaptable instrument for such a purpose. It should be noted, however, that the unconditioned salivary reflex is only one of many other secretory and motor reflexes elicited by food in the other organs of the digestive system and even other systems. On associating the extraneous stimulus with the food, a conditioned reflex is developed not only to the activity of the salivary gland under our special observation but to the whole complex gamut of reflexes in the other organs and systems which are not being es-

---

[1] I. P. Pavlov, *Lectures on the Work of the Cerebral Hemispheres,* p. 48.

pecially observed. By special experiments they can be easily discerned and studied.

But no matter how important the cortical regulation of the digestive activity in all its large scope may be to the organism, it does not cover by any means the manifold activity of the brain. And indeed, in Pavlov's laboratories and in the laboratories of several of his pupils and followers it has been established that *on the basis of any one of the numerous unconditioned reflexes to the activity of any organ there can be established a conditioned reflex.* For example, there have been developed and studied conditioned reflexes to the activity of the gastric glands, the pancreas, liver, kidneys, spleen, to the change in activity of the heart, vessels, and a number of other internal organs. Conditioned reflexes have also been developed to the motor defence reflex of an extremity evoked by its electrical stimulation, to the function of the respiratory muscles, etc. It is amazing how conditioned reflexes or conditioned reactions can be formed to a number of the most delicate changes in the organism. If, for example, a morphium solution capable of causing vomiting, dyspnea, drowsiness, and sleep is injected subcutaneously in a dog for several days, then the mere act of injection (subcutaneous introduction of a physiological solution, simply puncturing the skin, etc.) will be enough to cause the same chain of reactions: vomiting, dyspnea, drowsiness, and sleep. If, however, instead of the morphium, a solution of thyroxine in a dose sufficient to considerably augment the oxidative processes in the organism is introduced in the same manner into the dog, then the same manipulation of sham injection will now cause the thyroxine reaction, i. e., augmentation of the oxidative process. The introduction of a suspension of a weak culture of some definite species of bacteria in the abdominal cavity causes a specific cellular defence reaction (the accumulation of leucocytes in the area of injection). By repetition of this procedure there can be developed a conditioned reflex to this reaction, i.e., it can be evoked by the mere act of sham introduction of the suspension. It is possible to develop conditioned reflexes to pathological states of the organism, for example, to experimental convulsive fits, experimental rigour, experimental poisoning, etc.

Pavlov had every reason to say: "Thus, the temporary nervous connection is a most universal physiological phenomenon both in the animal world and in ourselves."[1]

There still exists another important difference between conditioned and unconditioned reflexes—*the difference in their central localization.* According to all evidence, unconditioned reflexes are formed in every part of the central nervous system whereas the ability to establish conditioned reflexes, and the ability for conditioned reflex activity is peculiar only, or almost only, to its highest parts. In dogs and the other higher animals conditioned reflex activity is the exceptional, or almost exceptional, function of the cerebral cortex. Experimental data, true, not very numerous, inclined Pavlov to the idea that, after the cortex has been extirpated as completely as possible, all existing conditioned reflexes in dogs should disappear irrevocably without leaving a trace, and that they should lose their ability to form new ones. In animals other than mammals, with a feebly developed cortex or without one, the conditioned reflex activity is carried out by the highest parts of their central nervous system.

At first, Pavlov was of the opinion that the conditioned reflex link in dogs is effected between the extraneous stimulus centre in the cerebral cortex and the food centre in the medulla oblongata. A schematic representation of this conception has been given by Pavlov himself. (Fig. 7.) The temporary or conditioned connection between the cortical areas of the sensory organs (C-C) and the food

[1] I. P. Pavlov, *Twenty Years of Objective Study*, p. 711.

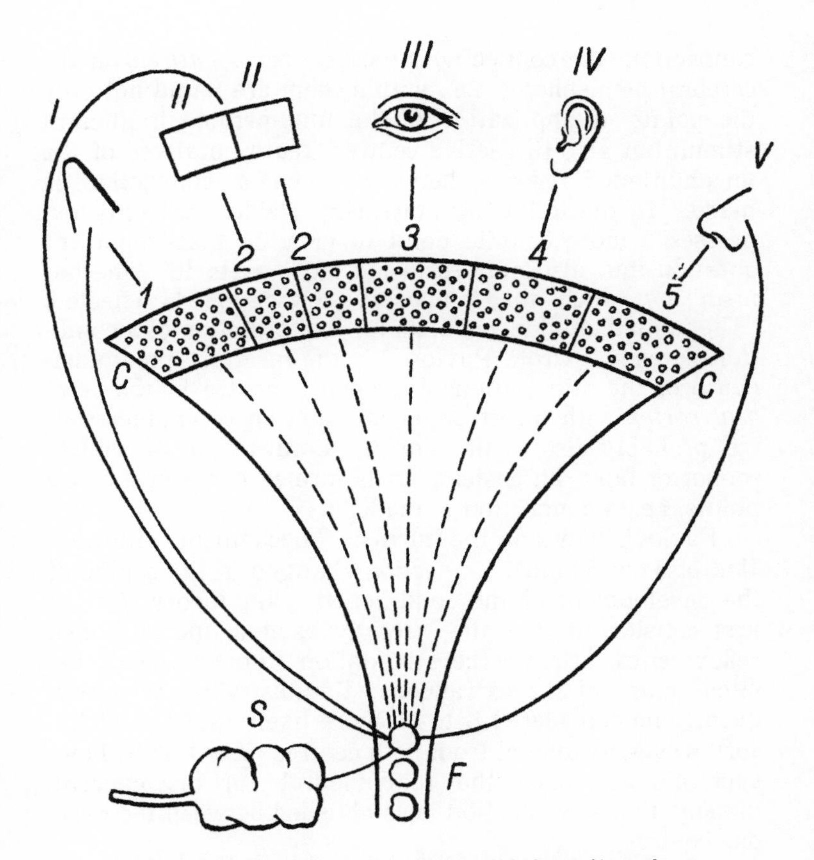

Fig 7. Initial scheme representing the formation of a conditioned reflex arc (according to Pavlov)

centre (F) are shown by dotted lines. Subsequently on the basis of certain indirect but more accurate data, he considered it more likely that the conditioned connection occurs entirely within the boundaries of the cerebral hemispheres, or, more precisely, in the cortex, between the extraneous stimulus centre and the cortical food regulatory area. Pavlov wrote: "The formation of a new nervous connection, the connective process, occurs *entirely* in the cerebral hemispheres, i.e., within them are found not only the points of application of the innumerable indifferent stimuli but also the active centres, representatives of the unconditioned reflexes, between which a connection is made." In the following statement, Pavlov not only expresses a more definite point of view on that important question, but also puts forth his ideas as to the "mechanism" by which the temporary connection is effected. "The fundamental mechanism for the formation of a conditioned reflex," wrote Pavlov, "is the meeting, the coincidence of the stimulation of a definite centre in the *cerebral cortex* with the stronger stimulation of another centre, probably also in the *cortex,* as a result of which, sooner or later, an easier path is formed between the two points, i.e., a connection is made."[1]

Pavlov's views on the intrinsic "mechanism" of formation of a conditioned connection changed in the course of the development of the conditioned reflex theory. (He at first considered that the strongly excited unconditioned reflex centre attracts the stimulation from the feebly excited centre of the extraneous stimulus, whereas subsequently he considered it to be more likely that the excitatory waves irradiated from both centres meet.) This, however, did not touch the fundamentals of his concept, namely, that a connection is established between the nervous centres.

Pavlov left no schematic representation of his new views on the location of the conditioned reflex connection. We have attempted, developing his ideas somewhat, to give them the schematic representation[2] shown in Fig. 8.

---

[1] I. P. Pavlov, *Lectures on the Work of the Cerebral Hemispheres,* p. 334.

[2] E. A. Asratyan, *The Anatomo-Histological Basis of the Conditioned Reflex Activity of Higher Animals,* Nature, 1937, No. 12, pp. 74-87.

The two different reflex arcs, from the eye to the muscle (for example, the neck muscle, as an element of the orienting reaction) and from the tongue to the salivary gland (as an element of the food reaction), are drawn separately in the figure. Each reflex arc is shown to be of

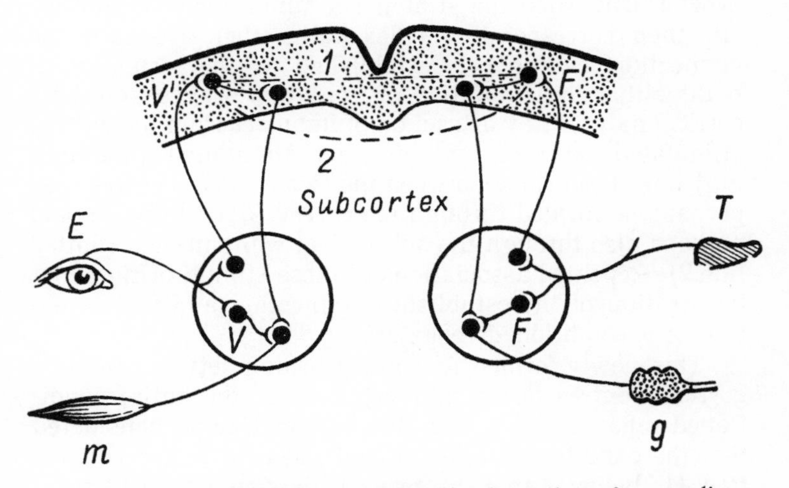

Fig 8. New scheme representing the formation of a conditioned reflex arc (according to the author)

EVM—The subcortical visory unconditioned reflex arc; EV^1M—The cortical visory unconditioned reflex arc, TFG—The subcortical salivary unconditioned reflex arc, TF^1G—The cortical salivary unconditioned reflex arc, $V^1 1 F^1$—The supposed location of the conditioned connection in the cortex, $V^1 2 F^1$—The supposed location of the conditioned connection in the subcortex

two levels (according to some evidence, in reality the levels are more in number), the lower arcs passing through the level of the "subcortical" (taken collectively) nerve centres ($E \rightarrow V \rightarrow M$) and ($T \rightarrow F \rightarrow G$) whereas the upper ones pass through the cerebral cortex ($E \rightarrow V^1 \rightarrow M$) and ($T' \rightarrow F^1 \rightarrow G$). The cortical elements of this arc are approximately what Pavlov termed the cortical representation of unconditioned reflexes. If a visual or gustatory stimulus is applied separately to the organism, then each of the bi-levelled arcs of these different reflexes will be excited separately and both reflexes—the motor reflex of the neck and the salivary reflex—will be separately evoked. But when the stimuli act simultaneously and excite their corresponding reflex paths, then a conditioned connection ($V^1 \rightarrow F^1$) is established by the formation of paths either by irradiation of excitatory waves from both cortical paths, or by attraction of impulses from the weaker stimulated centre to the stronger stimulated (dominating) one. The bridge between the two cortical centres may perhaps be formed through the cortex (dotted line 1) and perhaps also through the subcortical white matter (dotted line 2). Repeated associations of these stimuli bring about the fixation of the established connection and the formation of a conditioned reflex arc.

This newly formed temporary bridge between the two cortical centres forms the very base of the entire conditioned reflex activity. For this reason Pavlov considered that the conditioned reflexes could also be called *connective.* He believed that, in general, the newly formed nervous path could conduct in both directions, but according to all evidence, in the case of simple conditioned reflexes, impulses conducted preeminently in a single direction—from the feebly excited cortical centre to the stronger one ($V \rightarrow F^1$).

Thus by effecting a connection between the "cortical representations" (to use Pavlov's expression) of two different unconditioned reflexes an arc is formed of a new and higher type of reflex—of the conditioned reflex ($E \rightarrow V^1 \rightarrow F^1 \rightarrow G$). The conditioned reflex can, therefore, in our opinion, be defined or characterized also as the resultant of a synthesis or simply the *synthesis of two* (or more) *different unconditioned reflexes.*

It follows from the above-stated, that in its physiological role and significance the conditioned reflex appears to be the means for the cortical regulation or higher generalization (higher integration) of the functions of the organism. With the formation of each new conditioned reflex, the cerebral cortex more and more widens the limits of the higher generalization, the higher integration of the most complex functions of the organisms, increases its power over these functions. The result of all this is that "this higher part holds under its control all the phenomena taking place in the body."

By his studies, Pavlov not only enriched physiology with highly valuable facts concerning the specific properties of the new, higher type of reflex he had discovered, but firmly established the fundamentally important physiological principle that the development of conditioned reflexes of diverse types and orders is an essential function of the cerebral hemispheres; that these reflexes, as elementary psychical acts, jointly form the basic fund of the higher nervous or mental activity of animals. "Hence," wrote Pavlov, "with the discovery of the conditioned reflex, the main part and perhaps the whole of the higher nervous activity is placed in the hands of the physiologist."[1]

His ingenious mind generalized these original facts, treating them from a Darwinist point of view. Some advanced physiologists as early as at the close of the 19th century made quite successful efforts to comprehend the biological significance of a number of phenomena concerning the activity of the lower parts of the central nervous system according to Darwin's principles and certain of his direct indications, but the doors of cerebral physiology for long had been closed to the theory of the great biologist. Only Pavlov's genius threw them wide open.

[1] I. P. Pavlov, *Lectures on the Work of the Cerebral Hemispheres,* p. 32.

In his theory of the higher nervous activity there is shown with utmost clarity the enormous biological significance of the conditioned reflex activity in the struggle of the organism for its existence. According to the theory, whereas inborn or unconditioned reflexes are sufficient for the initial, rough orientation of the organism in a new situation (the so-called orienting reflexes) and for its crude adaptation to a more or less constant environment, the most delicate and perfect adaptation of the organism to the constantly changing environment is effected just through its conditioned reflex activity and is carried out by the formation (and if necessary, elimination) of conditioned reflexes of diverse types and orders.

Pavlov wrote: "As a part of nature, every animal organism is a complex, individual system, the internal forces of which, at every given moment, as long as it is existing as such, are balanced by the external forces of its environment. The more complex is the organism, the finer, more numerous and more varied are its elements of equilibration."[1] Further, as if elaborating upon this idea, he wrote: "The primary provision for effecting this equilibrium and consequently the integrity of an individual organism and its species is to be found in the simplest unconditioned reflexes (such as coughing resulting from the presence of a foreign body in the trachea) as well as in the most complicated ones, ordinarily known as instincts, such as the food, defence, sexual, etc., instincts. These reflexes are evoked by internal agents in the organism itself as well as by external ones; as a result the most perfect balance is effected with great precision. But the equilibrium achieved by these reflexes would have been perfect only if the environment were absolutely constant. Since, however, the environment is highly varied and at the same time in a constant state of fluctuation, the uncondi-

[1] I. P. Pavlov, *Twenty Years of Objective Study*, pp. 122-123.

tioned connections, being of a constant character, are, therefore, insufficient and must be supplemented by temporary connections, i.e., conditioned reflexes."[1]

Elsewhere, he wrote: "The external world surrounding the animal, continuously inciting conditioned reflexes on the one hand, is also, on the other hand, continuously suppressing them; screening them by other vital phenomena which at each given moment are more suited to the demands of the fundamental law of life—the equilibration of surrounding nature."[2] If it be taken into consideration that Pavlov understood by the term "equilibration" the delicate adaptation of the organism to its environment, then only from the viewpoint of the broad biological principle he was developing in these statements can we fully grasp the enormous biological significance not only of the temporary character of the conditioned reflexes but of all the other above described physiological properties that distinguish them from the unconditioned ones. If the fluidity, the instability, and fragility of conditioned reflexes, their utmost dependence upon their conditions, such as upon whether or not they are reinforced by unconditioned reflexes, make them a more pliable, mobile, and perfect means of adaptation to the infinite changes of the environment, then, owing to the signalizing character of the conditioned reflex activity, the organism strives to attain the conditions and factors favourable for its existence and avoid the unfavourable ones on receiving only remote presages of these factors—signals, conditioned stimuli. Furthermore, since each vitally important activity can be evoked by innumerable and varied conditioned stimuli, the signalizing or conditioned reflex activity broadens the field of perception of the external world and the scope of action in it.

---

[1] *Ibid.*, p. 710

[2] *Ibid.*, p. 127.

Constantly comparing conditioned and unconditioned reflexes, emphasizing their differences as well as the biological advantages of the conditioned reflex activity, Pavlov, as a true evolutionist, indicated at the same time the relative character of such differences between these two fundamental types of nervous activity. He stressed their evolutionary relationship and the possibility of transforming conditioned reflexes into unconditioned ones, if this is called forth by an urgent biological necessity. Pavlov wrote: "The cerebral hemispheres are an organ for the analysis of excitations and for the formation of new reflexes, new connections. They are the specific organ of the animal organism for establishing a more and more perfect equilibrium with its external medium, an organ to react directly and specifically to the varied combinations and fluctuations of the external world. It is, in a sense, a special organ for the uninterrupted development of the animal organism. *We may assume that certain of the conditioned, newly acquired reflexes can subsequently, through inheritance, be transformed into unconditioned ones.* (Italics mine.—*E. A.*)[1]

Hence, Pavlov's views on the decisive role played by the environment in the adaptative activity of the nervous system and, particularly, his opinion that individual reflexes may become fixed through heredity and passed on to succeeding generations as constituents of the fund of adaptative contrivances built up by the numerous preceding generations, are in complete harmony with the theoretical principles of Michurin, i.e., with the principles of Soviet creative Darwinism, now being furthered by T. D. Lysenko. True, Pavlov rejected the facts related to this question, which had been obtained by one of his collaborators through a faulty experimental technique, and the opponents of Soviet Darwinism have been speculating

[1] I. P. Pavlov, *Twenty Years of Objective Study*, p. 275.

I. P. Pavlov in the period of his work on blood circulation at the physiological laboratory of Botkin's clinics

I. P. Pavlov in the period of his work on digestion

on this. But we should bear in mind that it was the uncertain data of discredited experiments that were rejected and not the profoundly thought-out and advanced scientific principle. Pavlov remained true to it to the end.

For three decades Pavlov had studied the laws governing higher nervous activity almost exclusively in experiments on dogs, his traditional object of investigation. In the course of "nearing by stages" his original goal—the study of the higher nervous activity of man—in his last years he also took up with great interest an objective study of the behaviour of anthropoid apes (chimpanzees) occupying a rather high position in the evolutionary scale and by the structure and function of their nervous system much closer to man than dogs or the other members of the animal kingdom. Pavlov attached special significance to such an investigation from the standpoint of his materialist theory, too, because many foreign scientists (Chobehaus, Köhler, Yerkes, Lashley, et al.) were studying the behaviour of these animals from an idealist-psychological point of view, striving to strengthen the shattered positions of the latter by pseudo scientific theories. In complete contrast to the strictly scientific, objective, Pavlovian approach to the complex behaviour of anthropoid apes, the above-named scientists attempted to throw light on the internal world of these animals through the prism of the subjective feelings of human beings, attributing to the apes such human forms of mental activity as reason, imagination, the ability for an "intrinsic comprehension" of the nature of objects and phenomena, the capability of an instantaneous solution of complicated vital problems, and of solving unexpected difficulties owing to a "sudden dawning of the understanding." Such bothersome attacks on the philosophy of materialism, including Pavlov's theory, could not be disregarded, the more so since these idealists had amassed a considerable amount of rather interesting data and were making skilful use of them to give to their reactionary conceptions the appearance of an established, sound scientific theory.

In his work Pavlov gave due consideration to the higher level of the nervous activity of anthropoid apes in comparison to dogs. He took into account certain biologically important peculiarities of the organization and behaviour of apes, in particular, that: "the amazing mechanical adaptability of apes owing to the possession of practically four hands and a semi-vertical manner of walking placed them in a specific relation with their environment as compared to the animal world standing beneath them in the scale of evolution." Here he, therefore, employed his objective method for studying the higher nervous activity differently than in the case of dogs: namely, he developed an experimental technique wherein the fundamental indicator was no longer the salivary gland, but the simple and complicated motor reactions of the animal, which during the experiment enjoyed an almost complete freedom of movement and action. To obtain food, the ape had to surmount the most varied difficulties: to put out a fire barring the way to the food, or choose a suitable "key" and open the door of a box with food, or to build a stable pyramid of various-sized boxes, climb upon it and fetch the food hanging aloft, etc. The task of the experimenter was to observe attentively the way in which these problems were solved, to throw light on the physiological nature of the solutions, and reveal the moving forces and laws governing the behaviour of the animals under such experimentally complicated conditions.

Two or three years of strenuous effort on the part of Pavlov and his collaborators along these lines brought them outstanding success supporting his materialist theory with respect to a particular, though very important, question concerning the behaviour of anthropoid apes. True to his traditions, Pavlov did not hurry with the publication of these highly significant results, and subjected them much longer than usual to a thorough collective discussion among his staff, on his celebrated Wednesday colloquiums and in private talks within a narrower circle of his collaborators. However, in the very last months of his life, he considered it possible to prepare a report on that subject which he had intended to deliver at the coming international psychological congress in Madrid.

In Madrid Pavlov in 1903 had triumphantly announced to the world the birth of his great theory. In 1936 the voice of this giant of scientific thought, this passionate, militant materialist, the irreconcilable enemy of the adherents of the noxious philosophy of idealism, was to have sounded again. But death brought an end to these plans.

The gist of Pavlov's results can be briefly summarized as follows: The complex behaviour of anthropoid apes during these experiments depends precisely on the conditions of their existence, on the peculiarities of the "environment" established by the experimenter. The formation of complex motor habits in these apes, which make it possible for them to acquire food, takes place according to the principle of "trial and error," i.e., the accumulation of "practical experience," the formation of simple and complicated conditioned reflexes and is by no means the result of any primordial ideas, notions, judgments, rational tendencies, "the sudden dawning of understanding" or of any other mysterious forces, as had been and still is maintained by the followers of idealist psychology in foreign countries. The formation and fixation, the complicating and combining, the weakening and disappearance of these habits, as well as the relations and interactions of these processes, occur, in general, according to the conditioned reflex laws already brought to light with respect to dogs. Some deviations caused by the specificities of the motor system, the level of development and biological peculiarities of the animal, do not go beyond "variations on the main theme." In particular, it was established that a very important and even the chief role in the formation of the complicated motor habits in anthropoid apes, as well as their behaviour in general, is played by the receptors of the motor organs or the so-called kinesthetic reception and by no means by the visual receptors as claimed by the idealist psychologists. Moreover, it was found that these motor habits, developed according to the principle of temporary connections, are generalized in the cerebral cortex and can thus be employed by the apes in solving new problems.

These and other theoretical and practical results obtained by Pavlov added to the triumphs of the materialist understanding of complex vital processes up to the "very limit" in the form of mental phenomena. It was the triumph of the great Pavlovian concept over the groundless and fallacious idealist theories of a large and influential group of reactionary scientists from capitalist countries, a group with whom Pavlov had carried on a heated scientific polemic and relentless struggle. About them he wrote: "They evidently have the desire that their subject remain unexplained. How strange indeed! The mysterious is what is alluring to them. They turn away from that which can be explained from a physiological standpoint.... In this harmful, I would say—repugnant, desire to depart from the truth, psychologists of the type of Yerkes and Köhler employ such barren notions as for example that the ape went off, 'thought at leisure,' as a human being would do, and solved the thing. This is, of course, nonsense, child's play, unbecoming.... Now I maintain on the basis of studying these apes that their rather complex behaviour consists of associations and analysis, which I consider the basis of the higher nervous activity."[1]

In his last years, Pavlov reached his cherished goal —the higher nervous activity of man, studying it for the

---

[1] *The Pavlovian Wednesdays*, 1949, Vol II, pp. 386, 388, 389

most part in its pathological aspects. His long experimental work on the physiology, pathology, and treatment of the higher nervous activity of animals and the 5-6 years of intensive clinical study of mental and nervous diseases, yielded outstanding results not only promoting our knowledge of the nature of certain diseases of the human nervous system and their treatment on a scientific basis, but also of the specific properties of the higher nervous activity of man, in general. The classic exponent of natural science made a new, exceptionally valuable contribution to his theory of the conditioned reflex or signal activity of the higher parts of the central nervous system—the conception of the so-called second signal system of reality.

Although in the process of evolution of animals the conditioned reflex or simple signal activity of the nervous system is constantly developing and becoming perfected, still in the animal world this activity does not undergo any radical, any qualitative changes. In all animals without exception, whatever the level of their evolutionary development, the conditioned reflex or signal activity of the brain is the result of the direct action of the internal and external medium of the organism on its sensory organs. Pavlov was of the opinion that "in the animal, reality is signalized almost exclusively by stimuli—and the traces they leave in the cerebral hemispheres—coming directly to the special cells of the visual, auditory and other receptors of the organism."[1] This type of signal activity constitutes almost the entire higher nervous activity of animals and occupies an important place in the mental activity of a grown-up man.

"This is what we too possess in the form of impressions, feelings, and notions of our environment both in

---

[1] I P. Pavlov, *Twenty Years of Objective Study*, p. 722.

its natural and social aspects, with the exception of written and oral speech. This is the first signal system of reality and is common both to man and animals."[1] But this does not exhaust the higher nervous activity of man. "When the developing animal world reached the stage of man an extremely important addition to the mechanism of the higher nervous activity was made."[2] In connection with the development of man's work and social life "there originated, developed and became perfected to a very great degree signals of the second order, signals of these primary signals in the form of oral and written speech."[3] This qualitatively new system of signals of reality is characteristic only of the higher activity of man, it is "only peculiar to us"; "it has made us human" and has played an exceptional role in our conscious life. These signals of signals, *speech* or *words,* "represent an abstraction from reality and allow of generalizations, constituting our extra, *specifically human, higher mentality,* creating first an empiricism general to all men and then, in the end, science, the instrument of the higher orientation of man in the outer world and in himself."[4]

Summarizing the above, it should be said that while continually emphasizing the differences in nature and principle between the two types of nervous activity based on the formation of a temporary nervous connection—the conditioned reflex action and speech, Pavlov at the same time pointed out to their intrinsic connection, to the fact that "the fundamental laws established in the work of the first signal system should also govern that of the second."

* * *

---

[1] I P. Pavlov, *Twenty Years of Objective Study*, p. 722.
[2] *Ibid*
[3] *Ibid*, p 732
[4] *Ibid*, p 616

Pavlov did not limit himself to impeccable factual proof of the fundamental principle in cerebral physiology, viz., that conditioned reflexes, of various types and orders, jointly comprise the basis of the higher nervous activity of animals, and to its profound theoretical exposition. He raised the physiology of the brain as a whole to a high scientific level. "In physiology," wrote Pavlov, "the conditioned reflex has become the central phenomenon, by the use of which we can study with ever more completeness and precision both the normal and the pathological activity of the cerebral hemispheres."[1]

Ivan Petrovich Pavlov at the head of a large group of students and collaborators systematically and successfully investigated, for many years and particularly in the Soviet period, the laws of the formation and course of the higher nervous activity. These studies embraced the laws concerning the formation, fixation, and extinction of conditioned reflexes, their interactions, mutual connections, and transitions to one another; the properties of the basic nervous processes of the cerebral cortex—excitation and inhibition—the laws of the general and local, analytic and synthetic functions of the brain (i.e., the laws of the conditioned reflex or higher nervous activity making possible the most perfect adaptability of the organism to changes in the environment). Furthermore, Pavlov and his collaborators by means of the conditioned reflex method made a detailed study of the specialization and localization of functions in the cerebral cortex and of a number of important problems related to the cerebral activity such as the physiological basis of type and character, the problem of sleep and hypnosis, the fundamental laws in the experimental pathology and therapeutics of the brain, etc. Naturally, in this brief sketch, only a schematic and fragmentary account can be given of the wealth

---

[1] I. P. Pavlov, *Twenty Years of Objective Study,* p. 712.

of material obtained by such colossal experimental and theoretical work.

In accordance with the highly important role of the excitatory and inhibitory processes played in the conditioned reflex activity, this problem occupied the central position in Pavlov's investigations. Here also, it will serve as our starting point, with the reservation, however, that we shall dwell predominantly on the role of inhibition and its relations and interactions with excitation (the role of excitation in the formation and fixation of conditioned reflexes has been elucidated in the material already discussed).

The fundamental rule for the formation of a conditioned reflex, the coupling of an indifferent stimulus with an unconditioned reflex, has been mentioned here more than once. It need only be added that for the quick development and fixation of new reflexes, the extraneous stimulus should be much weaker than the unconditioned one and precede the latter. It is also important that, during the development of conditioned reflexes, the brain be alert and the health of the animal generally satisfactory. Together these requirements create the best conditions for exciting the extraneous stimulus centre and the centre of the unconditioned stimulus, necessary for the formation of a temporary or conditioned connection between them. Neglecting any one of these requirements may not only become an obstacle to the formation of new stable reflexes, but may even become the cause for the weakening and extinction of those already acquired.

There are many reasons for the weakening and extinction of conditioned reflexes, the chief of them having already been mentioned, namely, the application of the con ditioned stimulus without reinforcement by the unconditioned stimulus and the sudden action of extraneous stimuli on the organism, especially if they are strong and unaccustomed ones. A detailed investigation brought

Pavlov to the conclusion that in both cases the conditioned reflex does not vanish completely without leaving any trace (in other words, there is, strictly speaking, no abolition of the temporary connection), but it is more or less blocked in its functions by inhibition, the constant antagonist of the process of stimulation. Special investigations have disclosed that such a conditioned connection is retained for long in its peculiar, suppressed or masked form.

Departing somewhat from our subject, we note here that, owing to the outstanding classical works of our native physiologists, I. M. Sechenov and N. E. Vedenski, and of their followers, both here and abroad, it had already for long been known that the nervous system possesses the property of producing two antagonistic but inherently connected nervous processes—stimulation and inhibition. Further, it had been established that excitation is responsible for, or reinforces, the work of the lower nervous centres and of the organs under their control, whereas inhibition, on the contrary, stops or weakens if necessary the activity of these organs and centres. Finally, it has become known that both processes, i.e., the "starter" or reinforcing mechanisms and the inhibitory, weakening ones, are equally important for the uninterrupted and coordinated work of the numerous and diverse organs and systems. Pavlov not only showed that these two indissoluble antagonistic nervous processes are constantly to be found also in the cerebral hemispheres, and particularly in their cortex, but also investigated the entirely new and important properties concerning the formation and course of the processes of excitation and inhibition in the highest levels of the central nervous system.

Pavlov distinguished between two fundamental types of inhibition—the unconditioned or external type and the conditioned or internal one.

He called the inhibition unconditioned which is evoked in the cerebral cortex by the action of unaccustomed, extraordinary stimuli and which is of the same inborn nature as the inhibition in the lower parts of the central nervous system. The existence of such a type of inhibition in animals can be shown very simply by experiment. If during a normally proceeding experiment upon a dog an unfamiliar loud sound is made or an unknown object appears in its field of vision or, in general, a sudden change in the surroundings takes place, then the stable conditioned reflexes weaken or disappear. Such inhibition ordinarily occurs quickly and is retained for a relatively short time lasting for minutes and only on rare occasions—for hours.

Conditioned was the term used by Pavlov for the inhibition which arises in the cerebral cortex when a conditioned stimulus is applied in the systematic absence of, or belated reinforcement by, an unconditioned reflex, i.e., inhibition which, so to say, is developed anew.

It should be mentioned here that the very discovery of conditioned inhibition is one of the greatest achievements of modern neurophysiology. This type of inhibition of the conditioned reflex has several variations or, to be more exact, it can be evoked in a number of ways. It can be formed step by step, but still rather quickly, by the frequent, consecutive application of the conditioned stimulus without reinforcement. The conditioned reflex thus becomes gradually weaker and weaker and finally disappears altogether (is extinguished). The inhibition in such a case does not last for long—dozens of minutes or for some hours. But conditioned inhibition may become more or less chronic and stable if it is evoked by the conditioned stimulus not being reinforced from experiment to experiment for days, weeks or months. One way of doing this is called "the differentiation of stimuli." When one of two closely related conditioned stimuli in experiments (for instance 80 beats per minute of a metronome when 80 and 100 are employed) is applied from day to day without being reinforced by food, then, as a rule, this brings about a weakening and, subsequently, the complete extinction of the conditioned reflex to that stimulus. At the same time the conditioned reflex to the reinforced stimulus (100 beats per minute) remains active. It is quite apparent that here we are dealing with a very fine adaptability of the organism to a change in conditions. One of the stimuli ceases to be a signal of food, it stops being a reliable sign of its coming and it loses its conditioned or signaling significance. It is as if it were destroyed.

It may have appeared that now this stimulus has become an indifferent one to the dog, that it has merely stopped exciting the food centre and nothing more. Pavlov and his students have shown that this is far from true. When the stimulus is being applied, an active process is taking place in the cerebral cortex, but of an opposite character to stimulation and of different properties. It is this which according to the general laws of physiology is the process of inhibition.

Why is the weakening and extinction of a conditioned reflex not reinforced by an unconditioned one (as, for example, in extinction and differentiation) assumed to be caused by the development of inhibition, by a characteristic blocking of the temporary connection?

The answer is that the stimulus, formerly indifferent with regard to the food activity and then becoming conditioned, does not return (owing to extinction or differentiation) to its initial, indifferent status. It does not lose its conditioned significance, but acquires a completely opposite character—that of a negative conditioned stimulus. This is to be seen, in the first place, in the motor reaction of the animal to the stimulus. The application of the conditioned stimulus alone ordinarily causes the so-called positive motor reaction to food in a dog. It gets up, if it has been sitting, goes to the place where food has repeatedly been introduced, looks, now at the conditioned stimulus, now at the window in which the plate of food usually appears, wags its tail, makes chewing and swallowing movements, now and then shifts from one paw to another, whines and howls, etc. After the weakening or differentiation of the conditioned reflex, the conditioned stimulus alone not only does not evoke salivary secretion, but, as a rule, not a single one of the entire gamut of positive motor reactions to food. The animal either remains sitting indifferently or even turns away from the place where food is usually offered. A still more important fact can be established by special procedures. Under the innocent mask of "zero," i.e., of the absence of salivation, a very active nervous process is hidden, brought into being in the conditioned connection area after the application of the stimuli. This irreconcilable antagonist of the excitatory process can, for example, greatly weaken and even completely inhibit the unextinguished or undifferentiated reflexes to other stimuli—a light, a bell, mechanical irritation of the skin, etc. When a differentiated conditioned stimulus is applied together with any one of these stimuli, or before them, the conditioned reflexes, as a rule, become weakened by a third, a half, etc. Quite obviously, if the process occurring here was not a negative but a neutral one, no such thing would have occurred. Since, however, a strong conditioned reflex is weakened (i.e., there is a weakening of the excitatory process at its basis) Pavlov was entirely correct in concluding that the positive conditioned stimulus, not reinforced by food, had become an active inhibitory agent, giving rise in the cerebral cortex to a process just the opposite of stimulation, i.e., to inhibition.

The above can be summarized in Pavlov's own words: "Conditioned reflexes make much more intricate, refined and precise the relation between the outer world and the organism. Our life is overflowing with them. They are the bases of our habits, our education and our whole disciplined conduct. The next phase in the development of the relations between the environment and the organism is that conditioned reflexes, being in principle signalizers, are constantly being subjected to delicate correction. When they are not confirmed by reality, i.e., if they are not followed by the actual phenomena of which they signalize, then, as if in accordance with the principle of economy, they are abolished for the present or under the given conditions, continuing to exist at another time, under different conditions. This is brought about by a special nervous process which in the generally accepted physiological terminology has received the name of inhibition.[1]

It was because of these and similar facts that Pavlov called such transformed stimuli, negative or inhibitory stimuli, and the effect they produced, negative or inhibitory conditioned reflexes. The conditioned stimuli and reflexes described earlier he correspondingly termed positive. It was as if by this he wanted to emphasize the completely opposite biological roles of these two types of signaling stimuli, the opposite characters of the external reactions of the animal to them and, finally, the opposite inherent physiological nature of the nervous processes incited by them in the cerebral cortex. Pavlov wrote about this: "Thus there exist positive conditioned stimuli (Pavlov often used this term to denote the excitatory process.—*E. A.*), i.e., those causing an excitatory process in the cerebral cortex and negative ones, evoking an inhibitory process."[2]

From the wealth of factual material accumulated in Pavlov's laboratory, it follows that the relationship

---

[1] I. P. Pavlov, *Twenty Years of Objective Study*, pp. 359-360.
[2] *Ibid.*, pp. 714-715.

between the two basic and antagonistic processes in the cerebral cortex—stimulation and inhibition—is characterized by the same properties as those of the fundamental opposites in nature, for example, the relationship between the positive and negative in mathematics, mechanics, physics, chemistry, etc. "An unceasing struggle takes place" between stimulation and inhibition independently of the time and place of their contact, independently of whether they appear simultaneously in the brain centre or in sequence, whether they meet near or far from their point of origin, etc. But at the same time these two nervous processes, each active in its own way, appeared to Pavlov, "as different sides, different manifestations of one and the same process." It is as if they were "two halves of a single nervous process," mutually exclusive opposites, resulting from the bisection of a single nervous process. Furthermore, they are not only opposite and antagonistic, but there is much similarity in the manner of their formation and the course of their action and when speaking of them "we can conventionally speak of positive and negative stimuli." Finally, they can be transformed into each other; they are in a state of continuous motion, development, and interaction; they are the active and fundamental creative elements; virtually, the producers of the entire, highly complicated and manifold higher nervous activity.

Let us cite a few examples.

The disappearance of positive conditioned reflexes caused by the acute or chronic absence of reinforcement of their stimuli by an unconditioned reflex is nothing else but the transition of stimulation into its opposite—inhibition, a change in sign. This radical alteration of the functional sign does not proceed smoothly and easily, but in an intensive struggle of competing processes.

But the transformation of inhibition to excitation can also take place. The negative or inhibitory conditioned reflexes are just as temporary as the positive ones. As soon as the conditions promoting their formation and stabilization are interfered with, i.e., as soon as they become reinforced anew by the respective unconditioned reflexes, they will again gradually change to positive conditioned reflexes; passing through a course of quantitative changes, through various stages of struggle between the chief antagonistic processes, they again change their sign. It has been established by such and similar facts that conditioned inhibition upon which the negative conditioned reflexes are based is just as temporary a process and also has to be formed as the conditioned stimulus at the basis of positive conditioned reflexes.

Similar to the way in which positive conditioned reflexes can serve as the basis for the formation of new ones of the same kind, the negative conditioned reflexes can become the basis for the formation of negative ones. (To bring this about, indifferent stimuli are repeatedly associated with the negative conditioned stimuli.)

The rule of the algebraic summation of stimulation and inhibition in the cerebral cortex is not confined to cases of their mutual weakening on encounter. Each of these processes can add to itself and become strengthened on the simultaneous or successive combination or repetition of conditioned stimuli of the same sign (i.e., positive with positive and negative with negative). If, for example, a conditioned stimulus (a light) evokes a secretion of saliva amounting to 40 divisions (the volume of saliva expressed in terms of scale divisions) upon acting for 20 seconds, and a certain definite musical tone evokes a secretion amounting to 50 divisions, then their simultaneous application for 20 seconds can cause the conditioned secretion of 70 divisions. On the other hand, the repeated application of negative conditioned stimuli will strengthen the inhibition in the cerebral hemispheres to such an extent that it will lead to a drastic weakening or even complete extinction of almost all the positive conditioned reflexes.

The dynamic, active nature of stimulation and inhibition is very clearly shown, for instance, by their common property of spreading out from the point of formation to near and even remote regions of the cerebral cortex (the law of irradiation), interacting with the local processes, summing up with them algebraically and then leaving them as if receding to the initial point of origination (the law of concentration).

"The essential property of these two processes," Pavlov said, "is that, on the one hand, when they originate, they have a tendency to spread out, to occupy an undue area, whereas at another time, under corresponding conditions, they are driven into definite regions and are confined there.[1]

A vivid proof of the irradiation of stimulation is the so-called generalizing phase of the conditioned reflexes in the first stage of their formation. For example, in developing a food reflex to a certain definite sound stimulus (let us say, 100 beats per minute of a metronome), many other auditory and, at times, even visual or other stimuli, which had never been associated with the feeding of the dog, will at first, as if automatically, become conditioned food stimuli. This is explained as the result of irradiation of the stimulation from the cortical centre of the basic conditioned stimulus to the neighbouring and remote areas of the cortex, which, as if undergoing a secondary excitation, form a conditioned connection with the food centre, stimulated somewhat later. In time, the irradiation of the stimulation becomes more and more limited, it is more and more concentrated in the region of its formation and most of the secondary conditioned reflexes disappear, also automatically.

---

[1] I. P. Pavlov, *Complete Works*, Vol. I, p. 412.

Especially illustrative are the irradiation and concentration of the inhibitory process. After a single application of the negative conditioned stimulus (an extinguishing stimulus, differentiating stimulus, etc.), and still more if it be repeated, it often happens that also the continuously reinforced positive conditioned reflexes are weakened and at times temporarily disappear. Obviously the centres or their temporary connections have been subjected to the action of the inhibitory wave, coming from the point of application of the inhibitory conditioned stimulus. Often the course of these waves can be followed very closely. As is to be expected, the earliest to weaken and those suffering most are the positive conditioned reflexes to the stimuli which by their nature are close to the inhibitory reflex (this means that their cortical centres are situated close to each other) whereas those positive reflexes, responding to stimuli far removed from the inhibitory reflex and unlike it, suffer less. In the course of time, however, a gradual recovery of these, so to say, secondarily inhibited, positive conditioned reflexes begins to take place, but in the reverse order—first the reflexes to the remote and unlike stimuli, and then the reflexes to the near and related ones. An example may be given as illustration. Let us suppose that a dog has four tactile food stimuli *a*, *b*, *c*, *d* (vide Fig. 9); *a* is inhibitory and gives a zero effect; the other three are positive and each produces 15 drops of saliva in 20 seconds. If the inhibitory stimulus *a* is not employed during the experiment, the conditioned reflexes are more or less firmly retained at a definite level. But some time after the application of this inhibitory stimulus a gradual weakening of the conditioned reflexes to the stimuli *b*, *c*, *d* takes place, the reflex nearest to the inhibitory stimulus, namely *b*, being the first and the most to be weakened, then follows the somewhat more remote one, *c*, and, finally, the last one, *d*. If the inhibition evoked by *a* is a strong one, it can also weaken conditioned reflexes to auditory, visual and other unlike stimuli. The process of successive inhibition gradually weakens and disappears. But now the abolition of the forced inhibition takes place in the reverse order. First of all the conditioned reflexes to stimuli far removed from the inhibitory agent and unlike it are freed and later those close to it and of a similar nature. One can thus

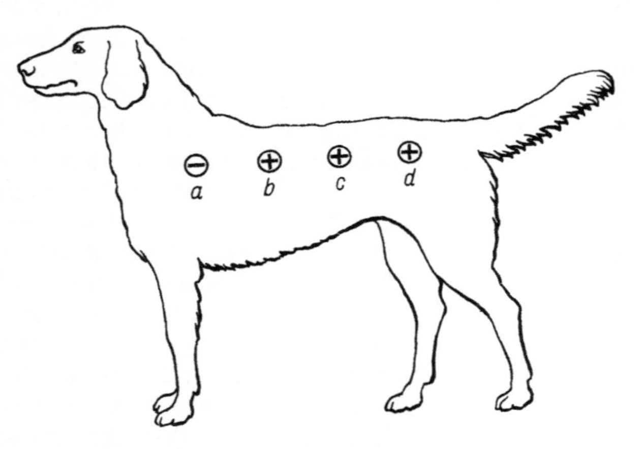

Fig. 9. Schematic representation of the "tactiles" on the body of a dog

follow the course of the inhibitory wave in both directions.

A certain detail is not without interest. The weak processes irradiate easily and relatively slowly, processes of an average intensity do not tend to irradiate considerably, whereas very strong processes irradiate as easily as the weak ones, but much faster and farther.

In the irradiation and concentration of the processes of excitation and inhibition is manifest one of the fundamental laws governing the function of the cerebral hemispheres in general, one of the basic forms of interaction and interconnection of the various parts of the cortex. The phenomenon of mutual induction (so called because of its superficial analogy to induction in electricity) is another kind of connection and interaction of the different parts of the hemispheres by means of these same processes. When a cortical centre is more or less strongly excited, the adjacent and even remote centres, as if by contrast, are inhibited. Vice versa, if the nervous centre be more or less strongly inhibited, the excitability of the other centres is increased. Induction can occur also in one and the same nervous centre. After its strong excitation, inhibition will set in and after a strong inhibition its excitability is increased.

Pavlov, by means of the conditioned reflex method, also discovered the laws governing the analyzing and synthesizing activity of the cerebral cortex. This activity is the result of the same two fundamental cortical processes, stimulation and inhibition. The conditioned reflex analytical and synthetical activity of the organism is the most perfect and most involved of all forms of such activity of the nervous system and is of a most considerable biological significance. Pavlov wrote: "Conditioned reflex agents, constantly and directly signalizing the favourable and injurious influences on the organism of its environment, are, in correspondence with the unlimited diversity and fluctuations of the latter, composed of both its minutest elements and larger or smaller complexes of such elements. This is made possible only because the nervous system possesses the mechanisms for discriminating, in behalf of the organism, from the complexity of the medium its separate elements, i.e., analyzing mechanisms, and for combining, fusing these elements into the various complexes, i.e., synthesizing mechanisms."[1]

---

[1] I. P. Pavlov, *Lectures on the Work of the Cerebral Hemispheres,* p. 100.

At first Pavlov's attention was drawn chiefly to the analytical function of the cerebral hemispheres, but with time he began more and more to explore their synthetical activity. "From the standpoint of the physiologist," he wrote, "the cerebral cortex is simultaneously and constantly fulfilling both analytical and synthetical functions, and any discrimination between the two, any study of one in preference to the other will not lead to real success, to a complete understanding of the work of the cerebral hemispheres."[1]

There are a number of forms of the simple and complex cortical analysis. They always start with the peripheral terminations of the analyzers (as Pavlov called the sensory organs) and end in the central terminations, i.e., in the cerebral cortex. One of the manifestations of a simple cortical analysis of the environment is the quite well defined direct relationship between the strength of the conditioned stimulus and the magnitude of the conditioned reflex. Up to certain limits, the stronger the stimulus, the greater is the reflex (the law of strength relations). However, if the stimulus is too strong, instead of a strengthening of the conditioned reflexes, a weakening sets in; whereas if stimuli are too greatly weakened the conditioned reflexes may instead of weakening at times gain in strength. The intensity of conditioned reflexes can be varied on increasing or lessening the unconditioned reflex. But the biological importance of the law of strength relations is not diminished thereby, since, first of all, it embraces the overwhelming majority of stimuli from the environment, and, moreover, a number of deviations from this law have other biological significance (the defence of the delicate cells of the cerebral cortex from the harmful effects of too strong stimuli, etc.).

---

[1] I. P. Pavlov, *The Physiology and Pathology of the Higher Nervous Activity*, Gosmedizdat, 1930, p. 36.

But the most perfect form of cortical analysis is intimately bound up with conditioned inhibition. An example of such analysis is to be found in the phenomena described here as the extinction of conditioned reflexes and, especially, as their differentiation and which were regarded as proof of the development of conditioned inhibition. By means of differentiation we can ultimately make a dog discriminate between 100 and 96 beats per minute of a metronome, between a circle and an ellipse with an 8:9 ratio of the semi-axes, between tones of 500 and 498 vibrations per second as well as between other very closely related mechanical, thermal, and olfactory stimuli. The loss of the specific signalizing properties by one of two closely related conditioned stimuli, if it ceases correspondingly to signalize the forthcoming event, and their retention by the other one are nothing other than the precise adaptation of the organism to its vital conditions through a most refined conditioned analysis by means of excitatory and especially inhibitory processes.

A proof of the perfect analytical activity of the cerebral cortex is also its ability to form different kinds of conditioned reflexes, i.e., to transform certain stimuli into conditioned food signals, others, into defence signals, etc.

Inherently connected with the analytical function of the cortex is its synthetic activity. Pavlov pointed out that the very fact of the formation of a simple conditioned reflex is proof of the higher synthetic activity, since, thereby, the cortex does not merely sum up two phenomena, but synthesizes two inborn reflexes into a reflex of a new, higher nature. The formation of conditioned reflexes of the second and third orders, as well as compound conditioned reflexes, i.e., conditioned reflexes to a complex of stimuli applied simultaneously or in succession, brings to light a still more involved and more perfect synthetic activity of the cortex. Finally, an expression of its supreme and most intricate synthetic activity is its ability to unite into a single unit the whole course of an experiment if, for several days in succession, the latter be performed by applying the stimuli in a definite order. In other words, it is able to automatize, so to say, the complex chain of the multifarious forms of activity. ("The dynamic stereotype" or systematization of the work of the cerebrum.)

Pavlov further demonstrated that the analytical and synthetical functions of the cerebral cortex are an integrate whole, that analytical and synthetical processes are always inherently connected with each other. This unity of analysis and synthesis comes clearly to the fore in the formation and specialization of a simple conditioned reflex. The organism combines or synthesizes two different stimuli which it differentiates from the mass of others. This becomes especially clear in the formation of a complex positive conditioned reflex to a definite sequence of a number of stimuli and of a negative reflex to another sequence of these same stimuli. The organism must simultaneously synthesize the stimuli into two different complexes and attach to them different functional roles.

The most striking illustration of the important biological role played by the analytical and synthetical functions of the cortex and of their indissolubility is that, in spite of the incredible complexity, diversity, and quantity of the processes occurring in the cortex, its work proceeds harmoniously. It functions as a single unit, and at the same time permits of the strictly differentiated activity of its parts. In general, its processes change and are systematized and coordinated in strict accord with the dynamics of the conditions of existence of the organism and with its current needs. And at the basis of this superb, manifold and at the same time highly labile mosaic of functions of the cortical activity lie various combinations of excitatory and inhibitory processes of varying intensity and length. "It is the balance between these processes," wrote Pavlov, "and its fluctuations within normal limits as well as beyond them which determine all our behaviour both in health and disease."[1]

However, the role of inhibition is not limited only to its participation in analysis and synthesis, to building up the coordinating and integrating function of the brain and the central nervous system, in general. Science is indebted to Pavlov for the discovery of an entirely new part played by inhibition, of a novel and highly important biological significance that it has for the nerve cells. The wealth of material from the long years of his laboratory experiments on animals and precise observations on human beings led Pavlov to the conclusion that inhibition also plays an important role as the organizer of the most beneficial physiological state of rest of the brain cells, the role of a natural defence factor of these cells against exhaustion and against the harmful effects of a number of disease-producing agents.

Many hours of wakefulness and particularly of intensive activity of these cells which are remarkable for their outstanding delicacy and fragility can cause their fatigue, weakening, and exhaustion. There is a limit beyond which such exhaustion can bring them considerable harm and even lead to their destruction. This danger is averted by the timely development of inhibition, i.e., by an active suspension of their functioning. "The cells of the cerebral hemispheres," wrote Pavlov, "are highly sensitive to the slightest fluctuations of the environment and must be carefully protected from overstrain, in order to be kept from destruction. For them such a safeguard is inhibition."[2] Hence, in this case, the role of inhibition is not in the organization (together with stimulation) of the concordant

[1] I. P. Pavlov, *Twenty Years of Objective Study*, p. 11.

[2] I. P. Pavlov, *The Physiology and Pathology of the Higher Nervous Activity*, p. 15.

action of nervous centres and their associated organs, but in the defence of the weakened and partially exhausted nerve cells. Inhibition provides them with that which they need most of all—rest, complete repose.

But this is rest of a special kind. It is not complete inactivity nor a suspension of the vital processes (nutrition, respiration, etc.). Inhibition apparently does not even slow down these processes to any extent. We may suppose that, essentially, inhibition blocks the cells, interrupts their connections with the other centres and organs and directs the function of the cells primarily as if along a different path, to the elimination of their own fatigue and other undesirable changes caused by lengthy and intensive work. It thus follows from Pavlov's theory that normal, periodic sleep is nothing else but just such a guarding or protective inhibition of the predominant mass of cerebral nerve cells. Pavlov wrote: "Sleep is an inhibition which has spread over a great region of the cerebrum, over the entire hemispheres and even lower down to the midbrain."[1]

A most simple and convincing proof of the truth of this conception concerning the nature of sleep is that it can be induced experimentally in animals by the repeated application of inhibitory conditioned stimuli, i.e., stimuli evoking inhibitory processes in the cerebral cortex. With each repetition of the stimulus, the inhibition at the point of formation is constantly strengthened. From there it spreads out to the other regions of the cerebral cortex, embracing them more and more widely and deeply.

Pavlov's theory not only explains the nature of sleep by a well-known physiological process—inhibition; but, better than any other theory, sheds light on its origin and development. The more or less equal fatigue of most of the brain cells creates a favourable condition for an

[1] I. P. Pavlov, *Twenty Years of Objective Study*, p. 385.

inhibition arising at any one of the cerebral centres to quickly spread over the entire brain. "Certain cortical cells reacting to the given external agent, which for long has been in action, and exhausting themselves, pass over into a state of inhibition, and, in the absence of any opposition by the other active centres of the cortex, the inhibitory process spreads out and produces sleep."[1]

Furthermore, many of the contradictions between the various one-sided theories as to the cause of sleep (exhaustion, the poisonous products of the vital activity of cells, the excitation of specific nerve centres, the cessation of impulses, etc.) have found their solution in the light of Pavlov's theory. The cerebral nerve cells are extremely sensitive to all sorts of changes both within and without the organism. They can be excited, weakened, brought to a state of exhaustion, and inhibited by a strong or protracted stimulation of sensory organs, nerves, and nerve centres as well as by all sorts of metabolic "refuse" of the organism; all these factors can favour inhibition and even produce it. In other words, they can induce sleep by acting on the brain, separately or in various combinations. Thus the exact facts of other investigators concerning the cause of sleep, considered from the viewpoint of Pavlov's theory, now no longer contradict, but supplement each other.

The influence of such sleep-producing factors as silence, darkness, monotonous sounds, quiet lying in bed, etc., is also satisfactorily explained by this theory. Some of these factors limit the external influences on the brain, whereas others act as conditioned stimuli causing sleep and developed by the conditions of the individual's life.

The defensive role of inhibition is brought to light with particular clarity in cases when a too strong stimulus,

---

[1] I. P. Pavlov, *Lectures on the Work of the Cerebral Hemispheres,* p. 226.

even if it is conditioned, is acting on the organism. The cortical cells in general are limited in their level of working capacity. If a stimulus is very strong and can produce an excitation transpassing this level, it would, if acting long enough, greatly exhaust the nerve cells. The timely development of inhibition in such centres serves to preserve them from further external influences (transmarginal inhibition).

There can be particular conditions of cerebral function (often reproducible in experiments on animals) when a superficial or sufficiently deep inhibition does not embrace the whole cortex, but only one or a number of its parts, causing sleep only in these parts. This peculiar partial sleep is just the physiological basis of hypnosis.

Thus, supported by exact facts, Pavlov referred the puzzling phenomena of sleep and hypnosis, which for centuries had been covered by a cloak of mysticism, to a well-known and elaborately studied physiological process. This is one of the immortal contributions of the great naturalist.

The conditioned reflex method proved to be also very fruitful in the investigation of a number of urgent and at the same time entangled problems of modern biology and medicine, related to the structural and functional characteristics of the brain. To such belong the specialization and localization of functions in the cortex, the type of the nervous system and the character of its function.

Pavlov irreproachably showed that there exists without doubt a localization and specialization of functions in the cortex. He thus proved the erroneousness of the metaphysical theory that the cortex is a homogeneous mass all of whose parts have the same functional significance. He also showed the inconsistency of the opposite, no less metaphysical, theory on this question.

It follows from Pavlov's flawless data that the specialization of functions in the cortex is not of an absolute or static character, but is relative and dynamic; that its boundaries are not narrow, nor defined by strict lines, but are wide and imperceptibly pass over into neighbouring zones. To be more exact, they are non-existent, since the zones overlap each other in their peripheral parts. The more specialized nerve cells are concentrated in the "nuclei" or "foci" of these localized cortical zones, whereas the less specialized ones are to be found in their broad periphery.

Lengthy observations upon dogs had furnished Pavlov with a wealth of material by means of which he was able to form a new conception of the physiological bases of the types of nervous systems and the character of nervous behaviour. According to this point of view, the type of the nervous system depends upon its congenital properties. There are three fundamental ones: viz., the strength of the basic nervous processes, excitation and inhibition, the equilibrity or balance of these processes, and, finally, their lability. Forming diverse combinations, these fundamental, inborn traits of the nervous system produce this or that type or temperament. Although, theoretically, a very great number of such combinations are possible (and consequently an equal number of types of the nervous system), actually, four clearly defined types are to be met with, which superficially coincide in many respects with the four temperaments already described by Hippocrates. These are the excitatory or impetuous type (choleric), the inert or slothful type (phlegmatic), the lively or active type (sanguine) and the weak type (melancholic). But, according to Pavlov's views, in the ultimate formation of the character of the nervous activity, side by side with these congenital characteristics a very important role is played by the changes caused by the life history of each individual, by the conditions of existence of the organism. Our nervous activity is like an alloy of these two forms of nervous behaviour, a synthesis of type and the influences of the environment. About this he wrote: "Type is the congenital, constitutional form of the nervous behaviour of the animal—the genotype. But since the animal is exposed from the very day of its birth to the most varied influences of the environment, to which it must inevitably reply by definite actions which often become more and more fixed and finally established for life, the ultimate existing nervous behaviour of the animal (phenotype, character) is an alloy of the characteristics of type and the changes produced by the external medium."[1]

It should be stated, moreover, that here also Pavlov considered the division of the properties of the nervous system into hereditary and acquired to be highly conditional and relative. For instance, on the basis of preliminary but quite convincing data, he considered it possible for the principal hereditary properties of the nervous system to be changed by external influences upon the organism and by its methodical training. It is not difficult to see that Pavlov's point of view is closely related in this respect to those of the outstanding representatives of Soviet Darwinism, I. V. Michurin and T. D. Lysenko.

In ending this very brief and schematic survey of the laws discovered and investigated by Pavlov, governing the normal function of the cerebral cortex, we may say: It follows from Pavlov's data that the various aspects of the cortical function and the nervous processes in the cortex are not separated, but are intimately connected with each other. They are in a constant state of interaction; they enter into diverse combinations, collide and clash with each other, are transformed to one another and as a result of all this create the integrate, harmonious higher nervous activity. Furthermore, the cere-

---

[1] I. P. Pavlov, *Twenty Years of Objective Study*, pp. 720-721.

bral cortex is constantly functioning in intimate connection with the other parts of the brain and even with the lower parts of the central nervous system, and such combined work forms the higher nervous activity.

It should also be mentioned that the laws discovered by Pavlov concerning the work and rest of the cerebral cortex are intimately bound up with those governing the work and rest of the lower parts of the central nervous system and even of the nervous system as a whole. Pavlov was of the opinion that the processes taking place in both the higher and lower parts of the nervous system are connected by a "natural unity," but at the same time, that most of the laws governing the work of the brain are different from those concerning the lower parts of the nervous system, being of a new, higher, and specific nature. For example, the conditioned reflex is an entirely new type of nervous activity. It also differs from the so-called "making of pathways," a general rule for the work of all parts of the central nervous system and an aid in the formation of conditioned reflexes. The internal or conditioned inhibition is also a completely new type of inhibition, differing from the inborn or unconditioned types, characteristic of all parts of the central nervous system. The course, interaction and interconnection of the processes of excitation and inhibition taking place in the cerebral cortex are also characterized by new properties. It is as if the laws governing the work of the cerebral cortex "repeat," on the higher curls of a spiral, the respective laws concerning the lower parts of the central nervous system and thus create a new, more perfect type of the adaptive or integrating activity of the nervous system.

* * *

A special place is occupied by the results Pavlov obtained in his theoretical and experimental investigations into the pathology of the cerebral hemispheres, as well as by the new principles he developed for treating the diseased states of the nervous system. Here also, the conditioned reflex method proved to be unsurpassed.

Pavlov was deeply convinced that "only by passing through the fire of experiment will medicine as a whole become what is should be, namely, a conscious and hence purposefully acting science";[1] that, in particular, experiments upon animals could be of great help to medicine in solving questions concerning the pathology and therapeutics of the nervous system. "The power of our knowledge over the nervous system will, of course, appear to much greater advantage if we learn not only to injure the nervous system, but also to restore it at will. It will then have been really proved that we have mastered the processes and are controlling them. Indeed, this is so. In many cases we are not only causing disease, but are eliminating it with great exactitude, one might say, to order."[2]

It is impossible, even in a most general way, to give here the rich, diverse, and outstandingly valuable results of the whole of this long, extensive experimental and clinical work of the great physiologist and physician on the changes caused by diseases of the higher nervous function and their treatment; a work so characteristic of Pavlov's creative nature, of his views on the union between theory and practice. But in order to give a general idea of the direction and character of these studies, we shall, nevertheless, refer to the most important of Pavlov's conclusions as to the factors responsible for the diseased states of the brain and the conditions favouring them, and then give a short account of his experimental data and general views on an important and, we may even say, the central question of his work in this field, concerning the

---

[1] I. P. Pavlov, *Complete Works,* Vol. II, p. 360.
[2] I. P. Pavlov, *Twenty Years of Objective Study*, p. 690.

role of inhibition in the origin of the diseased states of the cerebral hemispheres and in the treatment of such diseases.

Pavlov established that cerebral diseases in dogs can result not only from the crude, mechanical injury to the brain substance, but also from such actions that in no way impair its integrity nor the integrity of the organism as a whole. Such disease-producing factors are excessive irritations, such as loud noises, pain, etc., especially if they act more or less for a long time. Diseased states of the brain can also occur during a sharp collision between excitatory and inhibitory processes in the hemispheres, as well as under other influences on the organism, and in situations of conflict which demand too great an effort on the part of the hemispheres and are too heavy a burden on the cortex.

Pavlov also established that dogs most susceptible to such disease-producing factors are those with weak nervous systems and those of the excitable type. Dogs with a strong nervous system and with balanced excitatory and inhibitory processes are immeasurably more resistant in the face of such factors. Among the factors and conditions favouring the development of morbid states of the cerebral hemispheres can be mentioned hunger, exhaustion, infectious diseases, disturbance of the function of the internal secretory glands, etc. Depending upon the state of the organism, the nature, strength and duration of the pathogenic factor, and other causes, at times only the cells of definite cortical zones or even individual cortical centres are affected. But the disease can also affect the major part of the cells. Finally, of the greatest value is the fact brought to light by Pavlov, that the type of nervous system tells greatly on the character of the morbid state arising in the brain. One and the same disease-producing factor can cause diseases of the nervous system of dogs that completely differ both in nature and character, depending upon the types of their nervous system. Although there can be various degrees of abnormality of the affected nerve cells, two types of deviation from the normal corresponding to the two extreme types of the nervous system—the weak (inhibitory) type and the unbalanced (excitatory) type—are met with most frequently. In dogs with a weak nervous system, the pathological condition of the cerebral cortex is characterized, as a rule, by the extinction or considerable weakening of the positive conditioned reflexes and, in general, by a depression of the entire nervous activity and the functioning of the organism as a whole. In the excitatory type of dogs the pathological state of the cerebral cortex is characterized mainly by an extensive weakening or complete disappearance of the negative or inhibitory conditioned reflexes, by an excessive general excitation in the animal which may at times even lead to a state of aggressiveness. Both in the former and in the latter types of dogs, such abnormal activity of the cerebral hemispheres may last for weeks, months, and even years, depending upon the gravity of the disease and a number of other reasons.

Elaborate study of experimental pathological conditions of the cerebral hemispheres of dogs not only made it possible for Pavlov to demonstrate here a more striking protective role of inhibitory processes than in the case of periodic daily sleep, but brought him to an entirely novel and highly important discovery of the therapeutic role of inhibition.

In the normal life of a healthy animal or man, the onset of the protective inhibition of the predominant mass of cerebral nerve cells (in other words, normal sleep) ordinarily occurs in its proper time and thus eliminates the danger of their profound exhaustion. Such sleep is, moreover, of sufficient duration and depth to provide for a complete restoration of strength. However, the normal conditions for existence may be disturbed. The organism does

I. P. Pavlov in the last years of his life

The "tower of silence" at the Institute of Experimental Medicine

The house for anthropoid apes and for the study of their higher nervous activity (at Koltushi)

not always live in a state of well-being and cannot always avoid the action of harmful agents.

We have already seen that the fragile and delicate nature of the cerebral cells makes them very susceptible to all sorts of changes both within and without the organism. They are especially sensitive to violent changes, to abrupt pathogenic influences of a mechanical, chemical, or thermal character. If the body is exposed to a strong traumatic action, as in a traffic accident, a fire, bombing, shelling, or the like; if it is overheated by the sun; if it loses a good deal of blood; if some poisonous substance acts upon it; or, if an infectious disease begins to develop—in all such cases, almost always among the first to suffer are the brain cells, especially the cells of the cerebral cortex.

The organism in such cases has many devices for defence, among them, the protective inhibition. These devices are often successful in preventing a catastrophe, but not infrequently the struggle between the defensive forces and the pathogenic factors takes a serious turn for the organism. The protective inhibition does not always appear in due time; not always does it develop at a sufficient rate and with enough force to ward off the danger of a deep exhaustion of the brain cells. But once having appeared, it remains stable for considerable time, particularly in animals and human beings with weak nervous systems.

What is the biological significance of such a stable and long inhibition to nerve cells already injured or diseased?

Pavlov considered that it is of the utmost importance to the affected cells. Inhibition, first of all, protects them from the still greater harm which could have resulted had the cells continued their work. Secondly, it has a healing action on the diseased cells, restores their health.

"This quick functional destructibility," wrote Pavlov, "is the chief impetus for the appearance of a special inhibitory process in the cell, an economical process which not only limits the further destruction of its functions, but also promotes the restoration of the depleted excitatory matter."[1] Here inhibition not only plays the part of a means for the self-defence of the organism, i.e., as a "normal procedure of physiological control of the disease-producing agent," but also as a sort of natural remedy.

But cases are not infrequent when the protective and remedial inhibition which develops in the ailing cells is not strong enough to restore them to health. And even more, such cells may at times for some reason or other become extremely stimulated. A question then arises: since inhibition is an important natural remedy, can we not augment it, when it is not strong enough; or bring about its appearance, if it be absent altogether or only feebly expressed?

Pavlov and his collaborators gave a positive answer to this question, supported by scientific proof. They showed that the proper use of certain soporifics, in particular, bromine preparations, for reinforcing and extending inhibition (sleep) does, in fact, have a curative action on experimentally produced diseases of the nervous systems of animals. Writing, for example, about the action of bromine preparations on the pathological states of the cerebral hemispheres caused by the action of an excessive stimulus and the overstraining of the inhibitory process, Pavlov stated: "The extreme importance as a *curative factor* of the restoration and intensification of the inhibitory process is clearly emphasized in both cases, since, in addition to the experiments just described, many other experiments of ours show that to bromine should be

[1] I. P. Pavlov, *Twenty Years of Objective Study*, p. 445.

ascribed a direct bearing on the process of inhibition as just such a restorative and intensifying agent."[1]

It has also been established by Pavlov and his collaborators that a definitely positive influence on the recovery of the impaired nervous activity is exerted by such measures as a rest for the nervous system (a prolonged interruption of experiments on ailing dogs), a change in the character of the experiments, the elimination in the experiments of tasks demanding much nervous exertion, an improvement in maintenance, etc.

After long years of experimental and theoretical investigations into the pathology and treatment of the nervous system of animals, Pavlov, in the final period of his life, began a fundamental study of the problems concerning the mental and nervous diseases of man. The results of his "physiological excursions" into the most difficult terrain of medicine were outstanding. A fresh physiological spirit was brought into medicine. A new light was shed on the origin and nature of a number of diseases of the human brain; new ways were pointed out for their treatment. Essentially a new brilliant page was opened in neuropathology and psychiatry. Since the highly specialized character of these investigations makes it impossible to discuss their results here, we shall confine ourselves to only a brief account of Pavlov's contributions to the development and scientific grounding of one of the methods now prevalent for the treatment of the mental and nervous diseases of man—sleep therapy.

It frequently occurs in science that a number of investigators work simultaneously, independently of each other, on the solution of a certain problem. With time, their paths meet and their results serve to support each other. Something similar was the case in the work on the question of sleep therapy. Men of practice were heading

---

[1] *Ibid.*, p. 622.

towards the same goals as experimenter and theoretician Pavlov, and in the end their paths coincided. Pavlov came to the idea of treatment by sleep from the data of advanced science, whereas the practitioners, on the basis of many years of experience, in turn, came gropingly upon the tracks of this new therapeutical method. Physicians had for long been employing soporifics as sedatives and, recently, in the treatment of nervous and mental diseases. But failures were no less frequent than success. The attempts of treatment with the aid of soporifics had lacked a scientific basis. That important gap was filled by Pavlov's research and theories.

The fusion of age-old practice and advanced science took place when the great scholar was already at a very venerable age. But he was carried away with the ardour of youth by new methods of treatment and followed with the utmost attention the first successes in the clinical application of this method. Soon, the threads of his life were broken. But sleep therapy under the light shed by Pavlov's theory continues to make further progress.

In the very last years of his life, Pavlov planned a systematic experimental work of many years' duration on problems concerning the congenital and acquired properties of the nervous system and the evolution of the higher parts of the central nervous system. This extensive and interesting work was to have embraced the higher nervous activity of the chief links of the long evolutionary chain of the animal world with man at its head. To assure the success of the great thinker's plans and projects an entire scientific city was quickly being erected in the village of Koltushi near Leningrad. Deeply touched by the exceptional care and attention of the Soviet Government and the Communist Party, inspired by the rapid growth of his dearly beloved country's might, and eager to enhance the authority of his native science, the ardent patriot with passion so characteristic of him set out to realize his plans. He succeeded, alas, in carrying out only a small part of his magnificent project.

* * *

The more than sixty years of Ivan Petrovich Pavlov's work can be characterized as a triumphant march of blazing genius through the field of science. The great physiologist developed a powerful scientific method and by its skilful use was able to solve many of the most difficult and most involved problems in modern biology and medicine.

His versatile creative genius embraced a number of the most important fields of physiology and left an indelible trail. Pavlov's investigations into the physiology of blood circulation, digestion and the cerebral hemispheres; his profound and original theories of the trophic innervation of tissues, the physiology of the digestive glands and, in particular, the gem of all his work, his immortal theory of the higher nervous activity, constitute a complete epoch in biology and medicine. These great contributions of Pavlov placed the physiology of our country in the first rank of world science. They opened up wide vistas for its further rapid progress and outlined the directions for its forward movement.

Special emphasis should be laid on the enormous gnosiological significance of Pavlov's materialist theory of the higher nervous activity. Its import for the philosophy of Marxism-Leninism will be discussed in detail further on. Here we shall point out its significance for the nascent Marxist psychology. Pavlov created the groundwork for "physiological nervous deposits" and the premises for "superimposing the phenomenon of our subjective world" upon it for "fusing both together." He was of the profound belief that "the inevitable convergence and ultimate fusion of the psychological and physiological, of the subjective and objective is taking place and will finally be realized, and the question troubling the mind of man for so long will finally receive its *actual* solution. To further this fusion in every way is the important task of science in the very nearest future."[1]

By his rich, colourful, many-sided and original scientific work, unparalleled in the history of world physiology, Pavlov immortalized his name and brought glory to his dearly beloved country. He could rightfully say in the poet's words:

Unto myself a monument I raised not hand-created,
To it the people's path will ne'er be overgrown . . .

[1] I. P. Pavlov. *Twenty Years of Objective Study*, p. 535.

6. PAVLOV'S WORLD OUTLOOK AND THE SIGNIFICANCE OF HIS THEORY FOR DIALECTICAL MATERIALISM

Eminent theoretician in biology and medicine, Pavlov always attached much significance to the role of theory in the natural sciences. Throughout the whole course of his scientific work, the great thinker was constantly generalizing the wealth of experimental material he and his colleagues accumulated and he produced several profound and integrate physiological theories. Also he repeatedly made public his points of view on many important and essentially philosophical questions in physiology, biology, and the natural sciences in general.

All this provides us with considerable material for evaluating his philosophy.

Pavlov's views on the basic problems of natural science and philosophy and his world outlook, in general, are deeply rooted in the materialist traditions of the great Russian revolutionary democrats (Belinsky, Herzen, Chernyshevsky, Dobrolyubov, Pisarev) and their illustrious comrade-in-arms, the distinguished physiologist Sechenov. Constantly enriched, becoming more and more polished, these views did not undergo any significant changes during the entire course of Pavlov's long scientific career.

The great naturalist, too, had felt the mighty influence of the Marxist-Leninist world outlook.

* * *

Pavlov was a materialist. In his materialism he was fully conscious and not "intuitive," not "bashful" like the majority of eminent nineteenth-century naturalists and many modern foreign naturalists entangled in the maze of mysticism and metaphysics of decaying bourgeois philosophy.

His theory of the higher nervous activity is materialist not only in its objective content but also in its understanding and treatment of the nature and cause of the complex phenomena bound up with the mental activity of animals and man. In the cardinal problem of the relationship between matter and mind, Pavlov appears as a convinced, militant materialist. Advocating the necessity of extending the materialist principle of reflex action to include the higher nervous activity, a principle thanks to which "... an enormous field has been acquired for exact scientific research from the hitherto mysterious side of life," Pavlov said: "... And this is not a question of the absence of material facts, nor of a formula—both of these have for long been in existence—but of the universal recognition and systematic application of this formula in the study of the higher parts of the nervous system."[1] According to Pavlov's conception, any subject whatsoever under his investigation was always an element of material nature. He regarded all the complicated processes in the cerebral hemispheres as processes resting on a material basis. He considered that "function" and "dynamics" are intimately bound up with the "visible apparatus"; that they are "adapted to the finest structural details of the apparatus," that all the phenomena he studied existed objectively in time and space. Pavlov stated in his *Twenty Years of Objective Study* that the conditioned reflex theory is always concerned "... only with the objective facts, i.e., with facts existing in time and space."

[1] I. P. Pavlov, *Twenty Years of Objective Study*, p. 257.

"Our work, as in all other fields of natural science, rests on a sound basis of material facts."

On the cardinal question as to what is primary and what secondary—matter or mind—Pavlov took the stand of a materialist: "Consciousness appears as the nervous activity of a definite region of the cerebral hemispheres," or "mental activity is the result of the physiological activity of a certain part of the brain." Speaking of the complicated processes in the cerebral cortex, he wrote: "We explain this purely physiologically, purely materially, and purely spatially."

Characteristic of Pavlov's materialist standpoint is also his approach to the study of natural phenomena. As if in response to the words of Engels that: "The materialist outlook on nature means no more than simply conceiving nature just as it exists, without any foreign admixture," Pavlov wrote when beginning to develop his theory: "Natural science is the work of the human brain applied to nature and studying it with no assumptions or explanations from sources other than nature itself."[1]

Pavlov's conscious, militant materialism found a special colourful expression in his fiery polemics against animists, vitalists, dualists, and the psychologists and physiologists influenced by other varieties of idealism; in his energetic struggle for the uprooting of idealism and the triumph of materialism in biology and medicine, a struggle for the acceptance of the materialist point of view on the complicated "manifestations of living nature up to its very limit" in the form of mental activity in the most important and most involved question of natural science and philosophy—the relationship between matter and mind.

But Pavlov did not limit himself to a mere recognition of the truth of the fundamental principle of

[1] I. P. Pavlov, *Twenty Years of Objective Study*, p. 62.

materialism that matter is primary and mind, secondary, nor just to the brilliant experimental proof of its validity. The great naturalist was the first in the history of natural science to show experimentally that the higher nervous (mental) activity of animals depends upon the conditions of their existence, on their environment; that it has an "origin in experience" and is essentially the aggregate of the numerous conditioned reflexes of varied form and nature developed in the course of the life of an individual. This was exhaustively brought out by the results of his many years of research on the higher nervous behaviour of dogs and anthropoid apes. Supported by the data he obtained, he unceasingly carried on a relentless struggle against the adherents of idealism in physiology and psychology. He was imbued with the fire of youth, the passion of a militant materialist till the end of his life. Even at a very advanced age, in his very last years, his bitter enmity was not allayed to even a remote flavour of idealism. Relentlessly he attacked Lashley, Kathry, Köhler, Spierman, Sherrington and other foreign scientists for denying the connection between mental activity and the material structure of the brain, for denying the principle of causality in the higher nervous activity and, in general, for their idealist conception of psychical activity, "and their masked references to the *peculiar nature of mental phenomena*, behind which, in spite of the seemingly scientific arguments, can be detected dualism and animism."[1] Pavlov himself very correctly explained the negative attitude of Sherrington and other foreign idealists to his materialist theory of conditioned reflexes by the fact that it was directed "against dualist concepts—herein lies the whole reason; evidence of this are Sherrington's lectures, where he appears as a dualist, maintaining that man is a combination of two substances: the higher soul

[1] I. P. Pavlov. *Twenty Years of Objective Study*, p. 548.

and the sinful body. He publicly declares, strange as it may seem for a physiologist of modern times, that there may be no connection between the mind and the brain."[1] "Köhler is a confirmed animist," Pavlov declared with indignation on another of his talks on the "Wednesday" of September 12, 1934, "he can in no way be reconciled to the fact that this 'soul' can be grasped by hand, brought to the laboratory, and that the laws of its functioning can be ascertained on dogs. He does not want to admit this... Köhler is a victim of animism. Sherrington is another such victim."

The great naturalist considered these scientists as his ideological adversaries and proudly declared himself to be at war with them. "Now," he said, "we shall pass over from peaceful affairs to, if we may say so, matters of war, to M. Köhler. With him we are in conflict. This is a serious struggle. ... Among them there is apparently a desire for the subject to remain unexplained. How strange, indeed! The mysterious is what is alluring to them. They turn away from the possibility of an explanation from a physiological point of view...." At another time, contrasting the dualist and animist views of these scientists with his materialist monism, Pavlov said: "... the unmerited success of this psychology among modern psychologists can only be understood by assuming that among them dualism is still to be detected in the form of animism, i.e., the conception of the existence of a peculiar substance which is opposed to the rest of nature and with respect to which it forces the searching mind to hold itself otherwise than to the phenomena of matter."[2]

Only in the light of such antagonism by the materialist Pavlov toward idealism in whatever form it is expressed, can be correctly understood his true attitude to

---

[1] *The Pavlovian Wednesdays*, Vol. III, pp. 252-253.

[2] *Ibid.*, p. 44.

psychology, an attitude which had been misinterpreted not infrequently. In reality his enmity to psychology was essentially the enmity of an inexorable, militant materialist toward idealism which had found a retreat in psychology. Pavlov attacked the psychology of his time because of its anti-scientific, idealist nature, its indeterminism, because it considered the mind without regard to space and divorced the mental from the material. For this reason he characterized it as fantastic and barren. It was no mere accident that he constantly drew a contrast between psychology and natural science. For many years psychology was for him, so to say, the symbol of idealism, and natural science the symbol of materialism.

The conscious character of Pavlov's materialist views made itself felt in still another way. He considered it possible to solve the enigmas of nature. He was a great optimist and deeply believed in the omnipotence of the human mind, in its triumph over nature. Both his early and later works contain many superb thoughts, overflowing with this exhilarating optimism and directed against agnosticism, relativism and other forms of idealism. He wrote: "The complex is acquired by science only in parts and fragments, but gradually more and more completely. Hence, we will expect and patiently await the time when we shall really possess an exact and complete knowledge of the brain, and with it, also, the main grounds for sound human happiness."[1]

Pavlov was thoroughly convinced that the force of the scientific mind will bring about "such amazing discoveries and thereby such an extraordinary power over the higher nervous system as will in no way be inferior to the other achievements of natural science."[2] Establishing the legit-

---

[1] I. P. Pavlov, *Lectures on the Work of the Cerebral Hemispheres,* p. 345.

[2] I. P. Pavlov, *Twenty Years of Objective Study,* pp. 241-242.

imate right to scientific investigation of the mental activity of animals and man, Pavlov said: "I now, here also, merely defend and maintain the absolute and unquestionable rights of natural scientific thought, everywhere and at any time it *can* manifest its own strength. And who knows where the end of this ability lies!"[1]

Especially strong was Pavlov's faith in the might of experiment, the most effective and most trustworthy instrument for unlocking the secrets of nature, giving to scientific work its creative, active character. He maintained that in the course of the natural scientist's research "*observation* collects that which nature offers, whereas *experiment* acquires that which it desires." He believed that his investigations of the higher nervous activity of animals would be of considerable aid to psychologists in shedding light on the laws governing the mental activity of man. He was a strictly objective investigator of the complex phenomena of nature: in verifying his principles, he attached the decisive importance to facts. The criterion of truth he considered to be reality, the practical side of the matter. Pavlov, among his numerous reproaches to psychology and the psychologist, rebuked the latter also in that he "has not yet altogether rejected his partiality for the philosophical method of deduction, for pure logics without *verifying the conformity of each step with reality. The physiologist proceeds in quite the opposite way.*" (Italics *mine.—E. A.*)[2]

Only in this aspect can be fully appreciated the esteem of the great theoretician for precise, verified, reliable facts, for the mighty "Mr. Fact" playing, in his deep conviction, the predominant role in our quest for nature's secrets. His saying "facts are the air of the scientist, without them you will not be able to rise aloft, without

[1] *Ibid.*, p. 123.
[2] *Ibid.*, p. 537.

them your theories are vain efforts,"—should not be taken as manifestation of empiricism, as many do erroneously. These words are a vivid expression of a materialist outlook on the world. They express his view that the criterion for the verity of any theory is its correspondence with objective reality. Facts were for him a powerful armour defending his theory from the penetration of idealism.

That Pavlov's theory is of a materialist nature is fully recognized by bourgeois scientists and among them by such idealists as Sherrington and Trendellenburg. Sherrington, who even now still maintains that we have no right to link up mental phenomena with the physiological processes of the brain, once arrogantly told Pavlov that his conditioned reflexes will hardly be popular in England, because they have a materialist flavour.

Hence, it is quite obvious that Pavlov was a conscious materialist; he acknowledged the material nature of the objectively (outside of us) existing world; he considered matter to be primary and mind, secondary; he recognized that mental activity was dependent on the environment and experimentally proved this with respect to animals; he adhered to the opinion that even the most complicated phenomena of organic nature are open to our understanding; and, finally, he regarded the criterion of truth to be objective facts, experiment, reality.*

* * *

---

* An intrinsic part of Pavlov's militant materialism was atheism

According to a number of indications and above all to the questions constantly posed to those delivering popular scientific lectures on the life and work of Pavlov, there is a rather widespread erroneous opinion that Pavlov was religious. I shall allow myself to quote a number of his statements on that question.

Once in a circle of his collaborators in the winter of 1932, Ivan Petrovich stated definitely that he did not believe in God.

"When I was young, I was greatly disturbed by the question: Does God exist? After musing for long upon it, I came to the con-

What then is the nature of Pavlov's materialist outlook? It was immeasurably above a limited mechanist materialism and he wholeheartedly disapproved of the vulgar "shortsighted materialism which roughly and prematurely oversimplifies the subject and, thereby, depreciates

---

clusion that God does not exist. I reasoned as follows: Granted that God exists and that he is the creator of the universe. But who then created God?"

It unquestionably follows from such words that Pavlov was an atheist.

Furthermore, I heard repeatedly from Pavlov's own lips statements to the effect that a scientist cannot but be an atheist, that natural science and religion are incompatible.

He considered that popular education from a materialist point of view should supplant religion. His views on this he once expressed about as follows:

"There are still very many ignorant, uneducated people who understand very little of the phenomena of nature and social life and are deprived of such a strong moral support as enlightenment, education. The moral support in their life is to a certain extent religion, their belief in God. If we wish to take this support from them, we must supplant it by another—enlightenment—and then religion as a support will spontaneously disappear."

As to his desire that anti-religious propaganda carry to the people enlightenment from the viewpoint of materialism, it is in full accord with the principal demands regarding that question constantly advanced by our Communist Party.

As characteristic of Pavlov's attitude towards religion, highly interesting is also the following fact:

Some months before his death, Ivan Petrovich told a group of his collaborators that he had received a written invitation from a certain progressive group of English naturalists to become an honorary member of their newly formed society of "rationalists," which among other objectives had before it the task of waging a struggle against religion. Ivan Petrovich said that he answered as follows:

"I consent to become an honorary member of that society, provided that the struggle against religion be carried on by the propagation of enlightened thought."

All these statements clearly demonstrate Pavlov's atheism. He was an atheist not only in his views; his entire scientific work served to undermine the basis of religious philosophy.

it in the eyes of serious and sincere men."[1] A one-sided approach to the subject under study and a scholastic outlook on the causal relations between the phenomena of organic nature were alien to him. The motive power of his theory, its true philosophical essence, was dialectical materialism.

For 35 years the great naturalist studied by an objective and exact method, in a manner unparalleled in science for skill, singleness of purpose, and logic, the phenomena and processes in the cerebral hemispheres. He brought to light the complex laws governing their work, going more and more closely into them, "from the phenomenon," to say it in the words of Lenin, "to the essence, from the essence of the first order, so to say, to the essence of the second order, etc., ad infinitum." The true nature of his materialist theory was inevitably dialectical because "objective dialectics prevails throughout nature." (F. Engels.)

Here also, the conscious materialist Pavlov stood a head higher than the predominant number of noted naturalists of the last and present centuries. Not only is the wealth of data, on which his theory is based, objectively dialectical in content, he himself, as a rule, is dialectical in his generalizations and formulations of the laws governing the activity of the brain.

But before passing over to a concrete illustration of the dialectical essence of Pavlov's work, we shall say a few words about his scientific method which is basically dialectic from the standpoint of physiology as well as in its general theoretical aspect.

Pavlov is the founder of the so-called "chronic experiment" in physiology. He successfully employed this method first in his work on the physiology of the digestive system and afterwards with still more success in his out-

[1] I. P. Pavlov, *Complete Works,* Vol. I, p. 407.

standing investigations into the physiology of the brain. Contrary to all the old and the majority of new methods employed in the physiological research of the cerebral hemispheres, Pavlov's method of conditioned reflexes allows of an objective, all-sided study of the functions and laws of this supreme analyzing, synthesizing, and regulatory organ in its natural, intrinsic connection with all the other organs and systems of an intact organism. It permits one to investigate the processes occurring in the brain in their inherent connection and interactions, in the natural course of their formation and development. Pavlov's method makes it possible to study the processes of cerebral activity, as is required by dialectical materialism, "in their *'self-motion,'* in their spontaneous development, in their real life" (V. I. Lenin), to investigate objects, phenomena, processes "in their motion, their change, their life, their reciprocal influence on each other."[1] It provides the means for making a many-sided synthetic investigation of the functions of the brain and a filigree analysis of its activity. Pavlov's method is quite obviously dialectical in its principles and in its approach to the question and the material investigated.

Pavlov's views on the relativity of the classification of the objects and phenomena of nature as well as of the laws governing the inorganic and organic worlds also disclose a dialectical understanding of these questions. He wrote: "All our classifications, all our laws are always more or less relative and are of significance only for the time given, only under the conditions of the given experimental method, only within the limits of the material at hand." If we recall what has already been said regarding the absence in Pavlov of even a trace of agnosticism and relativism, it will be quite clear that for him the acknowledgment of the relativity of our classifications and laws

---

[1] F Engels, *Anti-Duhring*, Moscow 1947, p. 179.

and the relativity of our knowledge does not at all signify a denial of objective truth or the possibility of approaching it.

Now we shall pass over to the main point—the question of the dialectical nature of Pavlov's great discoveries in the physiology of the brain and the dialectic generalizations and formulations of a number of the most important principles concerning his materialist theory of the higher nervous activity.

It is opportune to recall that Engels characterized dialectics as the science "of the most general laws of mutual interaction," and J. V. Stalin, who raised dialectical materialism to a new and higher level, gave the following formulation of one of the main features of the Marxist dialectical method: "Contrary to metaphysics, dialectics does not regard nature as an accidental agglomeration of things, of phenomena, unconnected with, isolated from, and independent of, each other, but as a connected and integral whole, in which things, phenomena are organically connected with, dependent on, and determined by, each other."[1]

According to Pavlov's theory of the higher nervous activity, the complex and varied phenomena and processes occurring in the brain (the formation and course of positive and negative conditioned reflexes of the same and of different orders, the higher analytical and synthetical activity, the phenomena of the mutual induction, summation, irradiation, and concentration of excitatory and inhibitory processes and other aspects of its activity) are inherently connected with each other, are in constant interaction and mutually determine each other.

Further, the parts of the brain are in a state of constant, inherent connection and mutual causality and, to-

---

[1] *History of the Communist Party of the Soviet Union (Bolsheviks), Short Course*, 1952, p. 167.

gether with the brain as such, with the other parts of the nervous system, with the sensory organs, the endocrine systems, and with almost all the other systems. This is manifested in the strengthening of one group of conditioned reflexes and the disappearance of another, the predominance of one type of reflexes over those of another type, in changes in the nature of the fundamental nervous processes even up to their distortion, etc. All in all (and this should be especially noted) the entire activity of the brain is determined by its environment. The experimenter can evoke any type of conditioned reflex activity he has planned by combining stimuli in the specific "environment" of his box. It was not accidental that Pavlov called the principal form of activity of the cerebral cortex the conditioned reflex.

We shall give here a number of Pavlov's numerous statements on that question.

"The cerebral hemispheres are in their period of activity a system, all parts of which are in interaction with each other. . . . The cerebral cortex is a most complicated functional mosaic of separate elements, each of which possesses a particular physiological action, positive or negative. On the other hand, it is also quite obvious that all these elements are at every given moment combined into a system in which each of them is interacting with all the others."[1] In another place he wrote about this same subject: "Every new local influence on this system makes itself felt more or less throughout the whole system." After having described the laws governing the function of the cerebral cortex, Pavlov wrote further: "These phenomena have been described by us separately, as if they were independent of each other. But actually it is plain and logical that they should meet, combine, and interact."

---

[1] I. P. Pavlov, *The Physiology and Pathology of the Higher Nervous Activity*, 1930, pp 23, 35-36

Among Pavlov's writings one often meets with the phrase: "... According to the general law of interaction of the nervous centres." The choice of the attribute "conditioned" to designate the new type of reflex he motivated as follows: "By this attribute I desire to emphasize the characteristic objective property of these reflexes, namely, their extraordinary dependence upon a multitude of conditions, beginning with the conditionality of their origin." In another place he stated that the complexity of the conditioned reflex "consists not in any complexity of formation, but in the extraordinary dependency of the reflex on the phenomena of the internal medium of the organism as well as on those of the outer surrounding world."[1]

These examples are sufficient to form an idea of the dialectical nature of Pavlov's theories. He is also dialectical to the highest degree in his understanding of the relationship between the whole and the part. Enough to point, for example, to his theory of the dynamic localization of functions in the cerebral cortex, or to his conceptions of the mosaic pattern of the cortical functions.

According to Engels, dialectics is the science "of the general laws of motion and development of Nature, human society and thought." Developing this idea, J. V. Stalin gave the following definition of the second principal feature of the Marxist dialectical method: "Contrary to metaphysics, dialectics holds that nature is not a state of rest and immobility, stagnation and immutability but a state of continuous movement and change, of continuous renewal and development, where something is always arising and developing, and something always disintegrating and dying away."[2]

---

[1] I. P. Pavlov, *Twenty Years of Objective Study*, pp 259, 261.

[2] *History of the Communist Party of the Soviet Union (Bolsheviks), Short Course*, 1952, p 168

First of all, this peculiarity of dialectics found its expression in Pavlov's general views on nature as an integrate and unceasingly developing material system. "Before us," wrote Pavlov in his *Twenty Years of Objective Study,* "stands the superb fact of the evolution of nature from the primordial state in the form of nebulae in infinite space to the human being on our planet.... In living matter we see especially clearly the phases of evolution in the form of phylogeny and ontogeny." But still more strikingly did this feature of dialectics manifest itself in Pavlov's data and principles pertaining to the subject of his direct study—the physiology of the higher nervous activity.

His facts on the physiology of the brain vividly demonstrated that the processes in the central nervous system, in general, and particularly in the cortex, are not only intrinsically connected with each other and in a state of interaction, but are in incessant motion, development, formation and disappearance. It is just this extraordinary variability, mobility, and lability of their processes which is one of the characteristic features—one may even say the most characteristic feature of the activity of the cerebral hemispheres.

Not without reason, Pavlov sometimes designated the principal form of cortical activity as the "temporary" reflex. He often contrasted the cerebral cortex with the other parts of the central nervous system by just this property of their reflex action. In accordance with the external and internal media of the organism—various positive and negative reflexes are formed, develop and become extinct in the cerebral cortex; a complicated analysis and synthesis, the summation, mutual induction, irradiation and concentration of the principal nervous processes as well as other forms of cerebral activity are taking place. As a result, the organism quickly, nicely, and with great precision adapts itself to the constantly changing conditions of its outer and inner worlds.

This dialectics of nature found a vivid reflection in the principles formulated by Pavlov. We shall cite here a few of his numerous characteristics bearing on this question.

Referring to "the intrinsic mechanism of cerebral function," to its chief neural processes, Pavlov said: "The first thing to strike our attention here is the mobility of these processes." About the cerebral cortex he said: "Its activity is characterized by two principal features: extreme dependency upon conditions and as a natural result the lability of the processes constituting this activity."[1] On the peculiarities of conditioned reflex activity he spoke as follows: "The nervous processes we are studying are characterized by their lability; at every moment, with every new condition, they are assuming a new direction." Or: "The external world of the animal is, on the one hand, evoking conditioned reflexes, and, on the other hand, constantly suppressing them." According to Pavlov, "life is a constant interchange of destruction and rebuilding." Finally, he wrote that the brain "is the special organ for the unceasing further development of the animal organism."

Pavlov's highly valuable experimental material and certain of his principles serve as a natural-scientific proof also of that principal feature of the Marxist dialectical method which Stalin has formulated as follows: "... dialectics does not regard the process of development as a simple process of growth, where quantitative changes do not lead to qualitative changes, but as a development which passes from insignificant and imperceptible quantitative changes to open, fundamental changes, to qualitative changes; a development in which the qualitative

[1] I. P. Pavlov, *Lectures on the Work of the Cerebral Hemispheres*, p. 329

changes occur not gradually, but rapidly and abruptly, taking the form of a leap from one state to another; they occur not accidentally but as the natural result of an accumulation of imperceptible and gradual quantitative changes."[1]

The wealth of empirical material accumulated by Pavlov regarding the physiology of the conditioned reflexes shows that qualitative changes, transitions, leaps, are essential characteristics of the activity of the cerebral cortex.

The formation of a conditioned reflex, the fundamental "building stone" of the higher nervous activity, is in itself a sign of a qualitative leap in the process of development due to imperceptible quantitative changes such as the "making of pathways" or the dominant. The transition of positive to negative conditioned reflexes and vice versa, the development of the so-called transmarginal inhibition as the result of an excessive quantitative intensification of the conditioned stimulus (deviation from the law of the strength ratio of stimulus and effect), the directly opposite results obtained on the action of one and the same stimuli on the preliminarily changed background of the cerebral cortex, all these are some aspects of cortical activity which serve to illustrate the qualitative leaps in the process of its development.

Highly characteristic of the dialectical nature of Pavlov's theory is also the following: Generalizing an enormous amount of material, he came to the important conclusion that there is a "natural commonness" between the laws governing the activity of the higher and lower parts of the central nervous system. At the same time he constantly emphasized the specific character and qualitative peculiarities of the principal forms of function of the cerebral cortex. And in fact, if we look into the gist

[1] *History of the Communist Party of the Soviet Union (Bolsheviks), Short Course*, 1952, p 169.

of the matter, it becomes clear that almost all the fundamental laws concerning the work of the cerebrum differ from the analogous laws in the lower levels of the central nervous system not only in the degree of complexity, not only quantitatively, but primarily in their qualitative aspect. This refers to the difference between the lower analysis and synthesis, on the one hand, and the higher analysis and synthesis, on the other. It also concerns the difference in properties between the various unconditioned and conditioned reflexes as well as the differences in the lower and higher parts of the central nervous system between the fundamental nervous processes—excitation and inhibition, etc.

Pavlov established a "specifically human" type of nervous activity, the second or speech signal system, which according to an expression of his is the "extremely important" "when the developing animal world reached the stage of man."

Still another trait of Pavlov as a great thinker should be mentioned in this respect.

Holding to the opinion that science should aid man in solving important practical problems, Pavlov always gave a great deal of attention to experimental investigations of pathological and therapeutical problems and among them the pathology and therapeutics of the brain. But when it came to a question of applying to man the results of experiments on animals, the bold trail blazer in science became extremely careful, no matter what may have been the problem dealt with—the normal activity of the brain, its pathological activity or its medical treatment. He wrote about this: "If we must be cautious in applying to man our knowledge concerning the function of such organs in animals as the heart, stomach and other organs, similar as they are to those of the human being, and test the validity of the comparison by its agreement with the actual facts, then how great must be our reserve

I. P. Pavlov while speaking

The laboratories of the scientific city at Koltushi. On the right side of the building can be seen the inscription made according to Pavlov's instruction: "Observation and Observation"

I. P. Pavlov, K. M. Bykov, M. K. Petrova, I. P. Razenkov, V. V. Savich

I. P. Pavlov (fourth from the left in the first row) among his collaborators in 1935

in carrying over on man our only recently acquired exact scientific data on the nervous activity in animals. For it is just this activity which so sharply distinguishes man from animals and places him in such a dominating position in the animal world."[1]

All this unquestionably testifies to the correctness of the great scholar's methodological approach to the difficult question concerning the relationship between science and life including the application to man of the experimental results obtained on animals. It is well known that this has been a stumbling block for many prominent naturalists who took up either an idealist standpoint, separating science from life and denying the possibility of employing experiments on animals to solve problems in human physiology, pathology and therapeutics, or a standpoint of vulgar practicalism, mechanically equating the peculiarities of the physiological, pathological and therapeutical processes in man and animals.

Finally, Pavlov's data on the two fundamental antagonistic nervous processes—stimulation and inhibition and his profound generalizations regarding them, in particular, that these processes are parts of a united whole, that they are in a state of constant conflict and constant transition of the one to the other, and his views on the dominant role they play in the formation of the higher nervous activity—all these belong to the most established natural-scientific validation of the Marxist dialectical method. They are in complete accord with the Leninist concepts on the role of the struggle between opposites in the evolution, the motion of matter.

To illustrate the above we shall cite several of Pavlov's statements taken from his *Twenty Years of Objective Study*: "Nervous activity consists in general of the

---

[1] I. P. Pavlov, *Lectures on the Work of the Cerebral Hemispheres*, p. 345.

phenomena of stimulation and inhibition. They are, so to speak, its two halves." "Stimulation and inhibition are only two different sides, two different manifestations of one and the same process." "Inhibition constantly follows stimulation ... it is in a certain sense the reverse side of stimulation." "We can in a certain sense speak of positive and negative stimulation." "The basic processes on which this synthesis and this analysis rest are, on the one hand, stimulation and on the other, inhibition, a kind of direct opposite to stimulation." Differentiation or, in other words, the negative conditioned reflex, is, according to Pavlov, the result of "the struggle between stimulation and inhibition." This struggle is of a general character (disinhibition, breakdown, mutual induction, summation, the finer analysis and synthesis, sleep and wakefulness, etc.). More than that, according to Pavlov, "It is the balance between these processes and its fluctuation within and beyond their normal limits, which determines our entire behaviour, both in health and in disease."

Hence it can be said that from the standpoint of natural science Pavlov's facts and theory are vivid proof of the characteristic feature of the Marxist dialectical method as formulated by Stalin: "Contrary to metaphysics, dialectics holds that internal contradictions are inherent in all things and phenomena of nature, for they all have their negative and positive sides, a past and a future, something dying away and something developing; and that the struggle between these opposites, the struggle between the old and the new, between that which is dying away and that which is being born, between that which is disappearing and that which is developing, constitutes the internal content of the process of development, the internal content of the transformation of quantitative changes into qualitative changes."[1]

[1] *History of the Communist Party of the Soviet Union (Bolsheviks), Short Course.* 1952, p 171

Pavlov's theory of the higher nervous activity is an excellent natural-scientific support also for the Marxist conception on such dialectical categories as: chance and necessity (the formation of conditioned reflexes during a chance combination of stimuli and as a result—the transformation of chance to necessity); analysis and synthesis (the inherent connection between analysis and synthesis and their mutual interpenetration in conditioned reflex activity); form and content (the dependency of function on the material structure); causality (the strict determinism of all phenomena pertaining to cerebral function), etc. We could have cited as illustration many examples from the wealth of facts obtained by Pavlov and from his principles. We shall, however, limit ourselves to a single statement characterizing the way he understood most of these categories: "The theory of reflex action rests on three fundamental principles of exact scientific research: firstly, the principle of determinism, i.e., the impulse, motivation, cause for every given action or effect; secondly, the principle of analysis and synthesis, i.e., the initial disassociation of the whole into its parts or units and then the gradual rebuilding of the whole from the units or elements; and, finally, the principle of structure, i.e., the distribution of the action of forces in space, the adjustment of the process to the structure."[1]

From all the above it is clear that the factual content of Pavlov's teaching is thoroughly dialectical and that in his main principles he treats the nature and laws of the complex action of the brain from a dialectical standpoint.

* * *

What is the significance of Pavlov's theory of the higher nervous activity for Marxist-Leninist philosophy?

Actually, the answer to this question is already to be

[1] I. P. Pavlov, *Twenty Years of Objective Study*, p 547.

found in that discussed above; but we shall again touch upon it.

In connection with this question, it should be recalled that the great founders of Marxism-Leninism have always attached an enormous significance to natural science for the development of the materialist world outlook. Lenin wrote about that: "... natural science, reflecting the outer world in human 'experience,' is alone capable of giving us objective truth..."[1] In his book *Ludwig Feuerbach*, Engels concludes the survey of the history of the progress of materialism in connection with the development of natural science in the following words: "... Just as idealism underwent a series of stages of development, so also did materialism. With epoch-making discovery even in the sphere of natural science it has to change its form."[2]

Although Pavlov made numerous investigations which have become classical in a number of the most important branches of physiology, his crowning achievement is his work on the physiology of the brain and his theory of the higher nervous activity. The experimental and theoretical results obtained by him in the over thirty-five years of strenuous labour in this most complicated field of science are among the greatest landmarks on the highway of modern science leading to our knowledge of the deepest secrets of the brain, the highest, most perfect, and most complicated creation of nature. Unquestionably, they are of immense significance not only for physiology, for the many-sided activity of our socialist life, and for Marxist psychology, but also for Marxist-Leninist philosophy.

Further, the enormous amount of this valuable empirical material and the theory for which it served as the basis are very closely related to the *paramount ques-*

---

[1] V. I. Lenin, *Works*, 4th ed., Vol. 14, p. 113.

[2] F Engels, *Ludwig Feuerbach and the End of Classical German Philosophy*, Moscow 1949, p 24.

tion, according to Engels, *of all philosophy*—the question of the relationship between thinking and being, between mind and matter. This again serves to emphasize the prime importance of Pavlov's great theory for the philosophy of Marxism-Leninism.

We know that the only correct answer to this paramount question is that given by dialectical materialism, viz., "... thought is a product of matter which in its development has reached a high degree of perfection, namely, of the brain. ..."[1]

Engels and particularly Lenin gave a considerable amount of attention to the elaboration and natural-scientific proof of this basic principle of Marxist philosophical materialism, masterfully employing for this purpose all the most important achievements in cosmogony, paleontology, the theory of evolution, comparative anatomy, physiology, etc., of the 18th and 19th centuries.

The founders of Marxism-Leninism always regarded the material substratum of mental activity and mental activity itself from the standpoint of their origin and development. Owing to the evolution of matter, its "spontaneous motion" in a long series of evolutionary stages, owing to the origin and development of organic matter, the nervous system, and the sensory organs, there originated and developed from the elementary property of all matter—simple reflection—at first the simplest phenomena of irritability and subsequently more and more complicated forms of nervous and mental activity up to the highest manifestation of this activity, human consciousness, the result of socio-historical laws of human origin and development.

"But it is in the nature of matter," wrote Engels in the *Dialectics of Nature,* "to advance to the evolution of

---

[1] *History of the Communist Party of the Soviet Union (Bolsheviks), Short Course*, 1952, p 176.

thinking beings and hence this always necessarily occurs whenever the conditions for it are present." Lenin wrote the following: "Materialism, in full agreement with natural science, takes matter as primary and regards consciousness, thought, sensation as secondary, because in its well-defined form sensation is associated with the higher forms of matter (organic matter), while 'in the foundation of the structure of matter' one can only surmise the existence of a faculty akin to sensation."[1]

Engels and Lenin believed that the further progress of natural science would present more and more new demonstrations, new proofs of these views and, in particular, of the principle that the brain is the organ for the higher forms of mental activity. And, in fact, modern natural science has received a great many contributions serving as such proof. The most valuable of them are the experimental and theoretical achievements of modern biology associated with Pavlov's name. Herein lies the colossal significance of his theory for Marxist-Leninist philosophy.

In the first place, Pavlov, much more convincingly than his predecessors, experimentally demonstrated that the cerebral hemispheres are the organ of the higher mental activity, the organ for the most perfect adjustment to the surrounding medium. Then, he showed, on the basis of irrefutable data, that the higher nervous (or psychical) activity of the cerebral hemispheres also includes the regulation of the internal organs. In other words, they are or, rather, their cortex is, also the organ of the perfect adaptation and perfect regulation of the internal activity of the organism, of the processes taking place in the organs and systems.

---

[1] V. I. Lenin, *Materialism and Empirio-Criticism*, Moscow 1952, p 38.

It is, however, not this aspect of the experimental data and theories of Pavlov which is of the greatest value for the physiology and pathology of the cerebral hemispheres and for the philosophy of Marxism-Leninism.

Materialist views on the reflex nature of cerebral function were quite widespread among the naturalists of the middle of the 19th century.

But before Pavlov, the processes taking place in the brain had not yet been deciphered; the inherent nature of its function, the laws governing its activity, responsible for the higher nervous (or mental) behaviour, were still to be investigated. This was the problem which Engels and Lenin considered the most important and difficult task of natural science. The concepts in the nineteenth century prior to Pavlov were of a purely speculative nature. They were only bold conjectures and physiological outlines deprived of an experimental basis. Hence, they could not solve this problem even from a purely physiological point of view. The one-sided analytical method of studying nature and the discredited procedures of investigating the functions of the brain in parts (the artificial stimulation of the parts of the brain under the crude conditions of the vivisectional experiment, the impairing or extirpation of its parts) proved to be unsuitable for the solution of such a complicated problem.

And then the blazing genius of Pavlov appeared with a rich experience obtained in solving other profound secrets of organic nature; a genius, armed with a perfect synthetical scientific method and a delicate physiological technique, armed with new, exhilarating, and profound ideas and goals.

From the vague descriptions of this involved subject, from conjectures as to its nature, Pavlov went over to investigating its processes. In his study of the cerebral hemispheres, the great naturalist successfully applied that method of cognition which Lenin characterized as "the infinite process of deepening man's knowledge of things, phenomena, processes, etc., from the phenomenon to the essence and from the essence of lesser depth to the essence of greater depth."

Our great leader Lenin said at the outset of his revolutionary and theoretical work: ". . . as long as people did not know how to study the facts, they always invented a priori, general theories, which were always sterile. . . . The method itself was an absurd one. You cannot argue about the soul without having explained the physical processes in particular; here progress must consist in abandoning general theories and philosophical disquisitions about the nature of the soul, and in knowing how to put the study of the facts which characterize any particular psychical process on a scientific footing."[1] And this is what Pavlov achieved in his long years of work on the higher nervous system, if we are to give a most general appraisal of the quintessence of Pavlov's results.

Of immeasurable significance for the Marxist-Leninist philosophy is the "genuine physiology of the brain." With all the force of exact, reliable, scientific facts, Pavlov proved the existence of a material basis of mental activity and the dependence of this activity upon the conditions of existence of the organism; in other words that in the formation and development of the higher forms of mental activity the decisive role is played by the external medium: that mental activity has its "origin in experience." It can be confidently said that Pavlov's factual data and his theory of the higher nervous activity are the soundest support of Marxist philosophical materialism, namely, that thought is the product of highly organized matter, the product of the brain. Further, with the irresistible force of reliable data Pavlov also demonstrat-

---

[1] V. I. Lenin, *Selected Works*, Two-Vol. ed., Vol. I, Part 2, p. 112

ed the dialectical character of the processes in the brain, confirming once again "that in the last analysis nature's process is dialectical and not metaphysical...."[1]

Pavlov is the pride and glory of our science, the summit of natural-scientific thought. He was not only an unparalleled master of physiological experiment, skilfully unraveling the most entangled secrets of organic nature, but one of the greatest theoreticians in physiology, in biology as a whole, and in medicine. Contrary to most of the classic naturalists of the 19th and 20th centuries, he was not an intuitive, but a fully conscious materialist, an irreconcilable, enthusiastic fighter for materialism in the basic questions of natural science. Pavlov, with his skill as experimenter and profoundness of thought, contributed greatly to the triumph of materialism in natural science. It is difficult to overrate the significance of his theory for dialectical materialism. The rich data he obtained about the physiology of the brain are brimful with "objective dialectics." In his generalizations of this material, he advanced a dialectic-materialist explanation of the highly complicated work of the brain.

Pavlov's truly scientific, materialist theory of the higher nervous activity is a powerful weapon in our ideological struggle against the dark forces of reaction, against all manifestations of idealism and obscurantism.

And now, when the struggle between progress and reaction is becoming more and more intense, it is the duty of Soviet scientists to sharpen this weapon still more, to make it more and more formidable.

* * *

I. P. Pavlov bequeathed to his pupils and followers a very rich scientific legacy and outlined the ways for its further development. Owing to the exceptional

[1] F. Engels, *Anti-Dühring*, Moscow 1947, p. 39

attention paid by the Communist Party and the Soviet Government to the further development of Pavlov's scientific legacy, the facilities of his institutes and laboratories were greatly extended.

Thus all the prerequisites were provided for the further progress of advanced Soviet physiology.

The summer of 1950 saw the scientific session of the U.S.S.R. Academy of Sciences and the Academy of Medical Sciences, devoted to the problems of Pavlov's physiological theory. It was an outstanding event not only in our native physiological, biological and medical sciences, but in the scientific life of our country, in general. The reports of Academician Bykov and Professor Ivanov-Smolensky read at the session, as well as the numerous addresses by its participants, showed that Soviet physiologists have made certain progress in further developing Pavlov's scientific legacy. The following achievements in that field were cited in the resolution of the session:

"Pavlov's idea that all the important vital functions of the organism are regulated by the cerebral cortex has been broadly developed. These researches are of essential importance for the advancement of clinical medicine.

"New data have been obtained throwing light on the conditioned reflex mechanism in the behaviour of animals, and on the evolution of temporary connections. Definite progress has been made in the field of the pathophysiology of the higher nervous activity of animals and man, in elucidating the dependence of a number of pathological processes on the state of the cerebral cortex, and in determining the role of the cerebral cortex in the restoration of disturbed functions in the injured organism, as well as in the application of sleep therapy in various disorders.

"On the basis of Pavlov's theory of trophic innervation of the tissues, new data have been obtained regarding the trophic function of the nervous system. The Botkin-Pavlov idea of 'neurism' in pathology, the idea of the importance of the nervous system in the origin, course and issue of pathological processes, has been advanced. Pavlov's classical investigations of the physiology of the digestive processes have been carried a stage further. His ideas regarding the internal receptors of the organism are being developed."

In general, however, the resolution says, the works developing Pavlov's scientific legacy and particularly his studies of the higher nervous activity fall far short of the big expectations placed on the pupils and followers of the great scientist and are altogether incommensurate with the facilities provided by the Soviet Government and the Party.

The discussion at the session revealed significant shortcomings in the work of some physiologists and a number of scientific physiological institutions of the country, of the institutes and laboratories of the Academy of Sciences and of the Academy of Medical Sciences.

Having brought to light the causes of the shortcomings in the work of the Soviet physiologists in developing Pavlov's many-sided scientific legacy and severely criticizing the mistakes made, the joint session proposed a number of scientific and organizational measures for improving scientific research work. The resolution adopted at the session became the basis of the decision of the Council of Ministers of the U.S.S.R. to set up two physiological institutes within scientific institutions of the Academy of Sciences of the U.S.S.R.:

1) The Pavlov Institute of Physiology formed from the former Physiological Institute of the Academy of Sciences of the U.S.S.R., the former Institute of Evolutionary Physiology and Pathology of the Higher Nervous Activity, Academy of Sciences of the U.S.S.R., and the former Institute of Physiology of the Central Nervous System of the Academy of Medical Sciences.

2) A new Institute of the Higher Nervous Activity in Moscow.

A very responsible and honourable task stands before these institutes—the extensive creative development of the great Pavlov's scientific legacy, so dear and close to us all, and, particularly, his materialist theory of the higher nervous activity.

In accordance with the resolution of the joint session, *The Journal of the Higher Nervous Activity* was founded. A "Scientific Council on the Problems of the Physiological Theories of Academician I. P. Pavlov" was established at the presidium of the Academy of Sciences of the U.S.S.R. to coordinate and direct all the work in the country devoted to the development of Pavlov's theories.

The outstanding scientific discoveries of Pavlov, establishing the dependence of all forms of vital activity in the complex organism, including mental activity, upon the conditions of existence, advanced our native physiology to the first place in the world and opened up wide vistas for its further development. They created a firm natural-scientific basis for the advancement of medicine and psychology on new scientific principles. They contributed greatly to pedagogy and physical training and can add much to linguistics.

There are enormous forces of scientific workers in the Soviet Union, who are creatively developing and applying Pavlov's theories for the benefit of the people.